CONTENTS

ACKNOWLEDGEMENTS

This book could not have been written without the help and support of a great many people. First of all, Alan Cox, Chief Executive of ASW, agreed not only to support the research and writing of this book, but also to sponsor an exhibition on Steelmaking in Cardiff at the Welsh Industrial and Maritime Museum. As work has progressed I have been continually helped and encouraged by the enthusiasm and support of Roger Evans, Eira Purves and George Bartlett from Conway House, the headquarters of ASW, and by a great many people at the Training and Conference Centres at Castle Works. Particular thanks are owed to Teri Williams, David Harris, David Harry, Sharon Freeman, Phil Pratt and Caryl Kendell. I would also like to thank all the managers, personnel officers and others who have patiently introduced me to the mysteries of steel making and rolling, wire drawing and nail manufacture, showing me round the various works, answering questions and offering all kind of assistance.

This book is part of a joint project between ASW and the Welsh Industrial and Maritime Museum, whose keeper, Stuart Owen Jones, has been enthusiastic from the start. Robert Protheroe Jones, the research assistant there, not only collected and sorted Roy Stewartson's material, but has also allowed me the run of the museum's library and archive, as well as its picture collection, which is well represented here. Research for the book would have been impossible without the help of Edgar Jones, erstwhile company historian of GKN, who generously allowed me to rely heavily on his two-volume scholarly history, and I thank him. I would also like to thank the staff of public libraries in Dowlais, Merthyr and Cardiff, as well as at the Western Mail and the Glamorgan Record Office.

And so to the people whose testimony is an integral part of this book. They were not chosen by any particular method, but rather by word of mouth and happenstance. Before listing them, I would like to thank Bob Guppy and the members of the Linkage Association, many of whom have contacted with me with offers of pictures and information, and some of whom have been interviewed. A big thank you goes to the members of the Retired Officials Association who have welcomed me to their monthly lunches at St Mellons and regaled me with fascinating tales of the past. These, then, are the people I interviewed: Jim Ashford, George Bartlett, John Benson, Jack Bond, Arthur Bullock, Stan Carpenter, Colin Ceshion, John Collier, Alan Cox, Les Crocker, Joe Dacruz, Roy Davies, Roger Evans, Edgar George, Robert Gwynne, Ken Hutchings, Tom Keen, Gill Knowles, Ronny Knox, John Lockwood, Trevor Manley, Eric Osment, Frank Perks, Bill Redding, Paul Rich, Fred Roberts, Robert Spary, J J Sullivan, May Wace, Malcolm Wallace, Ivor West. Thanks are due to all of them, and also to Kate Fisher, who worked very hard transcribing the tapes, and has thus enormously increased their accessibility.

I must also thank David Evans, who nobly read through and commented on the final draft of the book, together with John Livsey and David Hughes who designed and printed it. A major thank you goes to the photographer David Lewis whose help in producing the illustrations for the book and the exhibition has been invaluable. Most of the illustrations contained here belong to ASW, or are in collections at the Welsh Industrial and Maritime Museum or the Glamorgan Record Office. Others have been donated by individuals, while the aerial views of Castle Works are reproduced by permission of H Tempest Ltd.

There are many people who are not mentioned here who have made offers of help which through sheer pressure of time I have not been able to take up. I

INTRODUCTION

I first met Roy Stewartson when my husband joined ASW early in 1991. Roy had worked for GKN and ASW for many years, and now that he had retired he was looking forward to devoting more time to collecting material for his proposed history of Castle Works. Since I am a trained oral historian, it was decided that he and I should record interviews with retired and continuing employees of the company who had stories to tell. Then Roy died suddenly, but such was the enthusiasm for his project that it was decided to complete it as a memorial to him, and this book is part of that memorial.

It isn't the book that Roy, with all his intimate knowledge of the company, would have written. I am not an engineer and I knew nothing of the history of the company when I started. However I have known Cardiff all my life and was quite willing to take over the project, particularly since before he died Roy had shown me much of his material – it is now in the archive of the Welsh Industrial and Maritime Museum. I have followed this up with my own research, and more importantly I have gone ahead with the interviews we had planned. Extracts from them are an important part of this book, and the tapes and their transcriptions have been deposited in the Welsh Sound Archive at St Fagans, to be a lasting record of the experiences of some of the people who worked in steel in Cardiff this century.

To a newcomer to Cardiff it may seem strange to begin the story of steelmaking in the city on Dowlais Top. But for many years the steelworks which stood next to Castle Works was known as Dowlais Works, long after the original works in Merthyr had been demolished. Indeed, as we shall see, the port of Cardiff developed partly in order to provide wharfage for the iron produced in Merthyr. Today those wharves and the old steelworks have gone, but still Cardiff thrives; and while the future of the docks area may still be a little uncertain there can be no doubting the present success of steelmaking, since ASW's Tremorfa Steel Works now produces more steel than ever was made in the city before.

PART ONE: THE GUESTS OF DOWLAIS

In general, in order to make steel you have first to make iron, and it is therefore not surprising that the technology necessary for large scale ironmaking developed some hundred years before that required for the manufacture of steel. In this first part of the story we shall see how ironmaking made first Merthyr, and then Cardiff as its port, into important industrial cities. Since Merthyr for a time led the world in ironmaking it is not surprising that it was quick to adopt new techniques for making steel, but in doing so it made inevitable the eventual transference of manufacturing activities to the more convenient port of Cardiff.

THE BEGINNING

In 1748 Lord Windsor leased a large tract of windswept mountainside above the tiny village of Merthyr Tydfil to one Thomas Morgan of Machen. Then as now Dowlais top must have been a desolate place, but appearances can be deceptive; like other inhospitable areas such as the Arabian desert or the North Sea it was what lay beneath the surface that mattered. In this case it was not oil, but a useful combination of iron ore, coal and limestone, together with plenty of rain and fast-flowing streams, which was to change the fortunes and the history of the whole of South Wales.

Even in those pre-industrial days, before factories, railways or steam engines, the mineral wealth of the land had been recognised. Thomas Morgan gained not only "all those mines and veins of iron and coal, and all Quarries of Stones, tyle and slate arising, growing or to be found in, upon or out of the land..." but also the right to "dig for, make and sink pits, and to make trenches, ditches, gutters, ponds and levels, and to erect limekilns for the burning of lime, engines, banks, stanks, sluices for the better scouring of getting, having and obtaining all such iron mine, coal and stone..." Yet whatever his rights, and despite the fact that he owned a small furnace at Caerphilly, it seems that Thomas Morgan ignored the subterranean riches of his new estate and contented himself with hunting over it. Indeed, nine years later he sold the lease to a partnership headed by Thomas Lewis, of New House in Llanishen.

There was no doubting the intentions of this group of people. Lewis already owned works at Pentyrch and Caerphilly, and was probably hoping to profit from the increased demand for iron resulting from the Seven Years' War. Moreover, Abraham Darby of Coalbrookdale had developed a technique of ironmaking which used coke as fuel, instead of charcoal. Since by now scarcity was forcing up the price of charcoal, it made sense to try out the new technology in an area rich in coal as well as iron ore. The venture must have looked promising, for soon the partners acquired further leases specifically for the purpose of erecting blast furnaces, mills, engines, kilns and coalhouses on land adjoining Dowlais brook, which was to provide the water power for their enterprise.

This plan of the first Dowlais furnace dates from 1763. The iron ran from the furnace (a) to the pig beds in the cast house (1). Wilkinson's blowing engine was at (3).

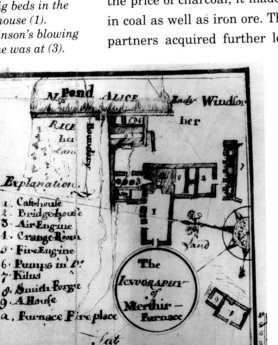

The first furnace was set into the mountainside, so that the burden (that is, a mixture of iron ore, coke and limestone) could be easily charged, by tipping into the open top; the molten metal was then run off at the bottom into the pig beds, reputedly so called because they looked like litters of piglets suckling from a sow.

In the early years, the components of the burden were obtained by scouring. A patch of mountainside rich in minerals was identified, and then a stream above it was diverted and dammed. When a sufficient head of water had built up, the dam

10

would be broken and the water would rush down the mountain, scouring away the topsoil and leaving the minerals exposed.

Coke, which was made by heating coal in an enclosed oven, was a far more satisfactory fuel than charcoal, since it could support a heavier charge of ironstone. It was also possible to build a larger furnace, and by the end of 1760 the furnace at Dowlais was producing an average of 18 tons of pig iron a week, which, with stoppages, gave a total of some 500 tons in the year. The blast required to increase the heat of the furnace was provided by a water-powered three-cylinder blower, newly patented by another Coalbrookdale ironmaster, Isaac Wilkinson, who was one of the original partners. Much of this iron was sold on to forges, where it would be reheated, and then hammered or wrought into shape.

JOHN GUEST

By 1767 the annual output had doubled. The enterprise was thriving, but it was clear that if it were to expand further the partners, who to varying degrees had interests elsewhere, would have to employ a full-time manager. Isaac Wilkinson had by now sold his share in the Dowlais partnership, but he recommended that the post be filled by an associate of his, also from the Coalbrookdale area, one John Guest.

Guest was born into a farming family, but his interests were wide. As well as brewing and coal dealing he had acquired the skills of smelting and refining, and operated a small forge. He and Wilkinson had already been involved in the Plymouth works in Merthyr, and he had acquired a local reputation as a canny businessman as well as a capable ironmaker.

Tradition has it that John Guest came to Merthyr on his grey mare, with his servant clinging on behind him. He was a Nonconformist, a man of simple taste who believed in thrift and hard work. When appointed to Dowlais he took up residence near the furnace. Every week English newspapers and letters from his family in Shropshire were delivered by a small girl, who much later recalled how she would find him sitting on a stone in front of the furnace. He was, she thought, "a tall, finely built man, with eccentric habits, but much loved by his workmen." This is not surprising, since Guest apparently lost no time in learning Welsh, and used to treat his workmen to an annual picnic – a practice that he stopped when he thought it was becoming an excuse for drunkenness. As soon as he felt that his position at Dowlais was secure he sent for his wife and children, and, perhaps more significantly, began to set aside money from his salary in order to accumulate shares. For John Guest and his family there was now no turning back; they had well and truly identified their fortunes with those of Dowlais.

THOMAS GUEST AND WILLIAM TAITT

When John Guest died in 1787, eight of the sixteen shares in the company were owned by his son, Thomas, and by his son-in-law, William Taitt. It seems to have been Taitt, rather than Guest, who was responsible for much of the development of the company in the next twenty years. Thomas Guest was a devout Wesleyan, a local preacher who rose every Sunday for prayers at 5 am. As a young man he had tried to improve the efficiency of the works, but he was thwarted by shareholders whose interests in the firm were in short term profits rather than long term investment, and this may well have contributed to his taking more interest in the construction of local chapels than in the maintenance of the works. It may also explain why early in the 1790s Guest and Taitt offered to sell out of the company, and when that failed proposed that it be taken over by its massive rival, Cyfarthfa Works. However, Richard Crawshay, owner of Cyfarthfa, was already sufficiently stretched to decline the offer, so that the only way forward was modernisation.

In 1790 the Dowlais Iron company was using water power to produce some 2000 tons of pig iron a year. However, there were now two blast furnaces, and the capricious nature of the water supply was a constant hindrance to steady output. One worker, writing in the nineteenth century, recalled his friends being required to tread the inside of the water wheel in order to keep it turning in times of drought or frost. In 1798, therefore, William Taitt decided to purchase a steam engine from Boulton & Watt; this was so successful that he bought two more. Not only did this provide a stronger and more regular blast for the furnaces, but it was also extremely efficient because the boilers of the steam engines could be fuelled by the small coals and slack which had to be removed from the mine but which were unsuitable for coking.

Taitt also pressed for the introduction of puddling and rolling, a process invented some twenty years before in order to produce wrought or bar iron. Pig iron was reheated in a furnace in which the fuel was burned separately from the metal charge, which was melted by heat reflected off the roof. When the metal became molten the carbon remaining in it was driven out, and gradually it began to re-solidify. To accelerate the process, the "puddle" of sticky metal had to be stirred with a long bar or rabble, until it formed a ball at the end. This task was performed by puddlers, highly skilled and necessarily hefty workers wearing heavy clothing to protect them from the intense heat. Similarly clothed shinglers then used huge pincers to carry the hot iron balls to the anvil, where they were squeezed to get rid of most of the slag, and then fashioned into rough bars. These were passed through rolls, some of which could be grooved to give bars of different shapes and sizes.

By waiting so long before adopting the new technology, the Dowlais ironmasters avoided the initial problems, and the construction of the most up-to-date puddling furnaces and rolling mills in 1801 meant that they were again competitive.

THE GLAMORGANSHIRE CANAL

It was all very well producing large quantities of iron, but this then increased the problem of its transport, for it was needed all over Britain. Within the immediate surroundings of the works heavy loads were carried on tramroads, the trams being drawn along the rails by horses. These were local journeys, however, and at the time of John Guest's death, every ton of iron that was sent to Cardiff for shipment elsewhere arrived on the backs of pack horses and mules. The cost was high, and the roads, given their mountainous nature and the vagaries of the weather, were treacherous. It was therefore not surprising that the Merthyr ironmasters, particularly Richard Crawshay, had strong interests in the construction of the Glamorganshire Canal, which opened in 1794. At the Cardiff end the mood was enthusiastic, as this extract from a contemporary newspaper relates:

> *The canal in this neighbourhood is completed; and last Friday a fleet of canal boats, from Merthyr Tydfil, laden with the produce of the iron works there, arrived at this place, to the great exultation, as you may imagine, of the town. With the iron treasures of the hills, we hope to grow daily more truly rich than the Spaniards are with their mines in Mexico and Peru...*

Certainly the canal benefited everyone, since it led to the establishment of Cardiff as a major port, as is shown in this account of 1805:

> *...a commodious dock has also been formed at the end of the canal, where vessels of large burthen may lie afloat...on the banks of the dock, spacious warehouses are erected by the proprietors of the ironworks.*

Crawshay exacted high tolls on the canal, however, and in 1802 the Penydarren Tramroad was opened, linking the other Merthyr ironworks to the canal at Abercynon, nine miles further south. It was on this track that, two years later, Richard Trevithick operated the first steam locomotive, which covered the distance in four hours. Sadly there were later complications which led to the project being abandoned, but inexorably the Railway Age was edging nearer.

THE WORLD'S GREATEST IRONWORKS

Thomas Guest died in 1807, and the management of the Dowlais ironworks passed into the hands of his twenty-two year old son, Josiah John. This young man had been brought up by an elderly nurse following the death of his mother, and had been sent back to Shropshire for his education. He had returned to Dowlais to learn the business, and although William Taitt did not think much of him at first, he left him his shares in the company. This meant that in 1815, when Taitt died, Josiah Guest was not only manager, but had a controlling interest in the business.

By this time the company operated four blast furnaces, but within the next twenty years no less that eleven more were to be commissioned. They were larger, too, and now stood away from the mountain so that the burden had to be hauled up by waterbalance lift capable of moving 500 tons of charge. In order to keep up with the demand for coal in the 1820s, massive workings were driven into the mountainside, one of which had its entrance in the very heart of the ironworks. Efficiency was further increased by adopting Neilson's hot blast process, by which the air blown into the furnace was first passed through hot bricks. In 1833 Josiah John Guest himself developed a running-out furnace, which meant that molten metal from the furnace could be run straight into the refinery, instead of having to cool off in the pig beds first.

The reason for this expansion is not hard to find, for by this time the early problems of steam locomotion had been eliminated and there was an enormous demand for iron rails. By 1821 Dowlais had won what was to become a world-

This picture shows workers at the furnace tops in Dowlais in about 1840.

wide reputation for the production of rails. In 1830 the Big Mill was laid down for the sole purpose of rolling rails, and this had to be supplemented by the Little Mill ten years later. During the 1830s orders for rails came from as far afield as Germany, Russia and America, and even the East India Company. In 1839 a new works, named after Josiah John's eldest son Ivor, was built next to the original one.

The Dowlais Iron Company was now not only the largest ironworks in Merthyr, nor even in Britain: it led the world. A visitor in mid-century left a vivid description:

The general view of these works is very imposing. Fourteen blast furnaces, fifty feet high, stand at the head of the area disposed in a curve something like the form of a horseshoe. Below these stand the refineries, and further down again, the mills and forges, with their hundred chimneys spouting forth fire.

SIR JOHN AND LADY CHARLOTTE GUEST

Josiah John Guest's early devotion to the works can be at least partly accounted for by the death of his young wife, Maria Rankin, in 1817. He was also able to enter politics, being returned to Parliament first of all for Honiton, and then, following the First Reform Bill, as the first MP for Merthyr in 1832. It was while he was in London on Parliamentary business that he was invited to the house of his business partner, and there met the twenty year old Lady Charlotte Elizabeth Bertie, daughter of the Earl of Lindsey. Within three months they were married.

It was a marriage that could easily have failed. The twenty one year old Lady Charlotte had been brought up in an aristocratic family in the depths of rural Lincolnshire. Although Josiah John was to be awarded a baronetcy in 1838, there was no disguising the facts that he was forty eight, that he came from a business background and that Dowlais House, her new home, was within yards of the ironworks. In addition, at the time of her marriage Lady Charlotte knew nothing of Wales, and nothing about ironmaking.

Yet this remarkable woman threw herself into her new role with enormous enthusiasm. In her journal she refers with affection to "the musical clank of bars and rails" and the "stirring and joyous mills". She was soon a familiar figure in the works, venturing underground, scrambling through the workings, climbing ladders, and even riding bareback on the tramroad horse... "as I bounded over the cinder tips and heaps of mine rubbish even they seemed to possess beauties."

Sir John Guest.

Lady Charlotte Guest

She insisted that her husband explain every process, read widely about the principles of ironmaking, and attended lectures at the Royal Society. In the space of thirteen years she bore ten children, all of whom survived, yet at the same time she acted as her husband's secretary, accountant and travelling companion. At Dowlais House she entertained a wide range of visitors, including her own rather baffled relations, foreign ministers of commerce, inventors, scientists and engineers. One of these was Isambard Kingdom Brunel, who worked not only on the Great Western Railway but also on the much smaller Taff Vale Railway, which joined Merthyr to Cardiff in 1841.

Lady Charlotte learned Welsh, originally with a view to conversing with the local people; she ended up translating The Mabinogion into English. Like many entrepreneurs' wives she took an interest in the moral welfare of the workforce, helping to organise the schools which her husband founded and even starting evening classes for adults, so that workers could catch up on education they had missed. On certain evenings there were parties to which respectable and skilled workers such as the puddlers were invited, so that they could mingle with employers and managers. Entertainment such as travel lectures, choir singing and piano recitals was provided.

LIVING AND WORKING IN DOWLAIS

Yet for all the enlightenment of the Guests, Merthyr and Dowlais were not attractive places in which to live and work. True, there was a certain grandeur in the furnaces themselves, particularly at night. A traveller in mid-century described the approach to Merthyr:

> *The traveller looks up...the very sky seems on fire – changing from deep red to brightest yellow...the light which he knows to be the furnaces of Merthyr, cheers and befriends him...above, glowing brilliantly, stands the vast circle of furnaces at*

Lady Charlotte addressing Dowlais scholars in the new school buildings which were designed by Sir Charles Barry, architect of the present Houses of Parliament. On special occasions Lady Charlotte had the buildings decorated with evergreens.

Dowlais; higher still...are the fiery domes of Ivor...the very stars look pale by contrast with the fires which burn below. The scene powerfully affects the imagination, for it has vastness, suggestiveness and mystery.

Within the works, however impressive, conditions were bad. By its very nature ironmaking involves heat and noise, but at this time there was no concept of safety and accidents were frequent. Hot metal caused not only severe burns but even the loss of limbs. Until 1842 it was not unusual to find quite young children in all parts of the works, opening furnace doors, working in the balance pits, piling hot rails ready for transport. A few years later the traveller described the work of a twenty one year old "Poll-girl"

My duty is to take the mine [iron ore] from the trams, to separate the stone from it, and then to pile it ready for the furnaces. I work eleven hours a day in the open air and am paid by the ton. My wages come to 3s 9d (17p) per week – not more. I clean and stack about four tons of mine a day. The mine is so flinty that it cuts my hands. I live on bread and cheese; often I do not get cheese; sometimes, but seldom, I have some meat for supper. I live at my father's; he is a miner. I cannot read or write. I was working very young to help my father and mother. There is but one bedroom in our house. My father, my brother, sister and myself all sleep in that room. We have three beds. My brother's age is nineteen.

Compared with some, that girl was lucky: there were many families with only one bed, and only one room to live in. The population of Merthyr had increased dramatically, mostly as a result of young people from all over Wales, but particularly the West, leaving the remote farms on which they had been born and coming to seek their fortunes in the town. As a result thousands of small houses **had been erected, many by the Guests. Although the people did their best to keep**

This picture from the Illustrated London News shows girls who worked at the Dowlais Works during the second half of the nineteenth century.

them clean, tidy and even painted, there was no running water, and this in a town where the majority of workers returned home so filthy that they had to wash all over each night. Fetching water was arduous, but more dangerous to health was the lack of drains, as the traveller found;

> *There being no town authorities to look to cleansing, draining and scavenging, the streets are in a state of disgusting*

filth, abounding in fermenting and putrefying substances, equally offensive to decency and injurious to public health.

Small wonder then that cholera was a visitor to the town, yet only after nearly fifteen hundred deaths in 1849 did Lady Charlotte Guest offer to pay for adequate drains. It may seem surprising to a twentieth century reader that the Guests, so liberal in many ways, were so oblivious to the plight of the workforce. Yet the prevailing economic theory was that the soundness of a business could be judged by its profits, and the best way of maximising profit was to keep wages low. In any case, according to the traveller, despite their poverty the ironworkers were on the whole sober and thrifty, and he describes the "promenade of the working classes" on a Saturday night:

> *All are dressed in their Sunday clothing, clean, warm and comfortable...Every face is smiling; pleasant greetings and friendly jokes are freely exchanged. All is happiness; the week's money is in the pocket...There are stalls of every description...Wandering about amongst these, accompanied by their wives bearing baskets, you see the sallow-faced hollow-eyed firemen, the noisy colliers, the prudent and saving miners, the jovial Irish labourers, all intent upon business, which they make a pleasure.*

THE CRISIS OVER THE LEASE

Even allowing for an excess of enthusiasm on the part of the writer, it is clear that the prosperity of the town depended on employment at the ironworks. It is hardly surprising then, that the 1840s were blighted by fears that Dowlais would have to close. This was not because it was unsuccessful; far from it. However, the lease of the once deserted mountain top was due to be renewed in 1848, and there was every sign that Lord Windsor's descendant, the Marquis of Bute, would exact a

This picture of the Dowlais Works shows a water-powered brick-making mill in the foreground, with the newly erected Little Mill in the middle distance.

bargain so hard that the Guests would give up the works. They had already bought a manor house in Dorset in full expectation of this eventuality.

Lord Bute's position was to an extent understandable. The rent he received for the land was minuscule in comparison with the enormous profits made by the Guests. Moreover, so abundant had been the seams of iron and coal that they had been worked wastefully for years, particularly when the expiry of the lease was imminent. Lord Bute regarded the Taff Vale Railway, of which Sir John was Chairman, as a deliberate means of depriving him of revenue from the Glamorganshire Canal, and he concocted vast schemes for the development of Cardiff as a port, financed largely by compensatory payments to make up for a century of lost rent. So obsessive was his suspicion of the Guests that he was forever changing his mind, and making totally unreasonable demands. By the December of 1847 Lady Charlotte had lost hope:

> *I wanted once more, while they were still in operation, to go through the dear old works, leaning as old on my dear husband's arm. I knew it to be my last day at Dowlais in its glory.*

Three of the blast furnaces were blown out, and the blowing engines were about to be dismantled when, forty four days before the lease expired, Lord Bute died unexpectedly. Lady Charlotte had a turn. "My agitation was so great that I could hardly breathe. Tears stood in my eyes and for many minutes I trembled violently." Ten days before the lease expired broad agreement was reached with the Bute trustees, and the Guests returned to Merthyr in June:

> *At the Lodge was a triumphal arch, made of flowers and evergreens and flags..When the carriage stopped Mr Jenkins read out the congratulatory address...(The crowd) then gave a number of cheers, some for him, some for me,some for the children, the works, the trade, the prosperity of Dowlais.*

SIR JOHN'S DEATH AND AFTER

For the Guests the triumph was short-lived, however. For some time Sir John's health had been failing, and though he went to Dorset to rest, in the autumn of 1853 he returned to spend the last months of his life in Dowlais, where he died in November. He was "a thorough man of business", according to the Gentleman's Magazine. Perhaps less objectively Lady Charlotte's memorial asserts that "through honest paths [he] placed himself at the head of the Iron Manufacture of Great Britain .... and was himself an example of what, in this free country, may be attained by the exercise of skill, energy and perseverance." Certainly his success at Dowlais was extraordinary. Even allowing for the fact that he was in the right trade at the right time, he must still be credited with the introduction of the latest technology, and the appointment of able managers. Only in the last years, which were overshadowed by ill-health and the expiry of the lease, did the works seem to falter.

It might have been expected that Lady Charlotte, devastated as she was by the death of her husband, and with ten children whose ages ranged from four to sixteen, would retreat to Dorset and leave the management of the works to someone else. But in the few years before his death Sir John had taken care to buy out his partners, so that the business passed directly to his widow, and Lady Charlotte was not one to avoid responsibility. The works had been allowed to deteriorate, and desperately needed firm management and investment, both of which she was to provide for the next couple of years, introducing new methods of coal extraction and firmly dealing with a strike. But it soon became apparent that her heart was no longer in Dowlais: indeed, in 1854 she made a determined but unsuccessful effort to sell the company. The reason was soon made clear: she was about to astonish her contemporaries once again by marrying Charles Schreiber, whom she had engaged as tutor to her eldest son Ivor.

It was this marriage that was to end the active part which had been played by the Guests in the Dowlais company for almost a century. Lady Charlotte, recognising that both the company and the Dorset estate would eventually pass to Ivor, left Dowlais House forever, returning only on visits. She and Schreiber were to travel around Europe, collecting china, and later she was to turn her attention to fans and playing cards. She spent her last years knitting mufflers for taxi drivers. Ivor, like so many sons of great industrialists, distanced himself from the enterprise that had been the foundation of his wealth, based himself in Dorset and London, becoming an MP and eventually being awarded the peerage that had eluded his father. Nor were any of the other Guest children to return to Dowlais, though several married into the great families of the aristocracy. Three

Dowlais House, built a stone's throw away from the Works in 1817. Here Lady Charlotte raised her ten children. Later on it became offices, and then was demolished in 1873.

generations of Guests had devoted their lives to a company which they eventually owned entirely; it is perhaps not surprising that the lure of the countryside eventually proved stronger than the flames and furnaces of Dowlais.

STEELMAKING AT DOWLAIS

The withdrawal of the Guests from Dowlais meant that the running of the business had to be undertaken by professionals, and in 1856 the trustees appointed as general manager a man who was to become one of the most distinguished of all nineteenth century engineers: William Menelaus. He did not waste time in assessing the problems of the company. "Dowlais is standing still instead of taking the lead," he reported in November 1857, and recommended further investment and innovation. Within the next few years furnaces were repaired, methods of coal extraction were improved, and new pits sunk. At the end of 1859 the huge Goat Mill was opened: capable of rolling seventy-foot rails, it was "thrice the power of any mill in the kingdom."

However the real advance under Menelaus was one which was to restore Dowlais' fortunes completely: the adoption of the Bessemer steelmaking process. Within the works puddling was always a problem, since greater output meant more puddling furnaces, and since the work was both unpleasant and arduous, it was becoming increasingly difficult to persuade young men to take it on. Therefore when The Times carried an account of Bessemer's process, which converted pig iron into molten steel without using fuel, Menelaus hurried to London and within a fortnight had obtained the first licence to use the Bessemer patent.

At first there were problems. The process involved blasting air through a giant ladle full of molten pig iron, causing a violent chemical reaction which gave off heat. In the course of this the slag was completely driven off, thus giving a much purer metal than was possible with puddling. Unfortunately the high phosphorus and sulphur content of the Dowlais iron meant that the first rails broke, much to the delight of the puddlers. However the supplies of local ore were dwindling, and within the next ten years the problems had to some extent been overcome: the converters were lined with silica bricks which enabled them to be charged with pig iron made from low phosphorus ore brought in from Cumbria and Spain. In July 1865 the first Bessemer rail was rolled at Dowlais, and by 1869 the company had six 5-ton converters. The days of the wrought iron rail were numbered.

The Bessemer process was not the only new technology to be adopted. In 1875 Menelaus built a Siemens-Martin open hearth furnace. This operated by heating a mixture of steel scrap and pig iron in a furnace fired by the gases produced during coke making: the gases then given off were used to heat the incoming fuel and air. The great advantages of this process, which was much slower than the Bessemer converter, were that it saved greatly on fuel costs and was much more controllable, so that steels of particular chemical compositions could be made for specific tasks.

With new technology and increasing output it was necessary to find new sources of ore, and in 1873 the Dowlais company purchased a share in the Orconera Iron Company at Bilbao. This ore was almost free of phosphorus and sulphur, and well-suited to the acid-lined furnaces at Dowlais. Vast quantities of ore were shipped through Cardiff, but although this meant cheaper production costs it only served to emphasise Dowlais' location problems.

It was not only that ore had to be transported from Cardiff to Dowlais, and that rails had to make the same journey in reverse. The world had changed. Britain had led the industrial revolution, but now other countries were catching up. Ironmakers in Germany and America could build integrated plant on open sites. The Dowlais Iron Company, pioneer though it had once been, could not compete. In 1882 Menelaus died, and within five years his successor, E P Martin, was planning the establishment of "Dowlais by the sea" – steelmaking was to come to Cardiff.

Perhaps the most logical move would have been to let the old works at Dowlais run down, and to have encouraged its workforce to migrate the twenty miles or so to Cardiff. But Ivor Guest, Lord Wimborne, who still took a paternal if distant interest in his company and the community of which it was a part, was not prepared to cause further suffering to people who had borne the brunt of the ills of industrialisation. There would be a new works at Cardiff, but the works at Dowlais would remain.

Furnacemen sitting on one of the Dowlais furnace tops at about the turn of the century.

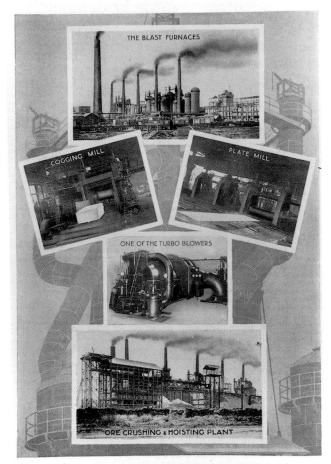

This page from a contemporary GKN booklet shows various activities at the Dowlais Cardiff Works in the 1920s.

PART TWO: DOWLAIS, CARDIFF AND ROGERSTONE

Though the origins of primary steelmaking in Cardiff, the "heavy" side of the industry, can be directly traced to Dowlais and the Guests, yet other strands in the story are to be found in the Midlands, where the "light side" – the manufacture of iron and steel goods such as wire, screws and nails, had long been established. In this part we shall see not only how the great Dowlais-Cardiff works were established, but also how the village of Rogerstone emerged as a site not only for steelmaking, but more significantly for the rolling of rod and other products which were to prove vital in the Cardiff story later on. Also, since we are moving into the timespan of living memory, it will be increasingly possible to draw on the recollections of people who were actually there at the time.

DOWLAIS – CARDIFF

The land which was purchased for the new works at Cardiff was beside Roath and East Bute docks, as well as being close to the mainline railway to Paddington. It was known as East Moors, for moorland it still was: a contemporary photograph shows the three new blast furnaces rising from a large expanse of tussocky grass. The ironworks was opened by Lord and Lady Wimborne in 1891, while the steelworks started production some four years later. There were six open hearth furnaces, and, since railmaking was well-established at Dowlais, slabbing and plate mills were laid down to provide plate for shipbuilding. Significantly the hearths were still lined with acid silica, to suit the low-phosphorus ore from Spain, whereas most steelworks in Britain had adopted the Gilchrist Thomas method, lining hearths with "basic" dolomite, which enabled them to utilise local high-phosphorus ores.

This picture, taken in about 1890, shows the moorland nature of the new Dowlais Cardiff Works.

Nevertheless, whatever its imperfections, this was one of the most advanced and integrated steelworks in Britain. The blast furnaces, originally 75 feet high, were eventually extended to 85 feet, and became a familiar landmark on the Cardiff skyline. Hydraulic power was used not only to hoist the charge to the furnace tops, but to raise ore from the cargo ships at the docks. In starting from scratch, E P Martin, who designed the steelworks, was able to plan the movement of materials to fit in with the latest manufacturing processes.

But though the works was to prosper, there was no avoiding the fact that the competitive forces which had inspired the building of Dowlais Cardiff still existed. Moreover, with the death of Lady Charlotte in 1895, and the passing away of the original trustees, the links with the glory days were diminishing. Lord Wimborne, though undoubtedly well-intentioned, was neither a business man nor an engineer. The prospect of being ultimately responsible for an enterprise the size of the Dowlais Iron Company with its enormous plant, to say nothing of extensive collieries, must have been daunting in the extreme for

Building the new steelworks at Cardiff, 1890.

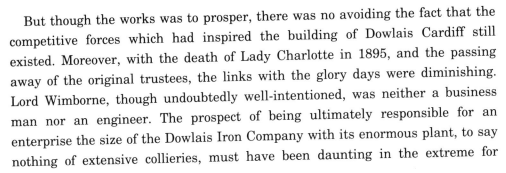

someone more at home in his Dorset mansion.

It is hardly surprising, therefore, that in the closing years of the century Lord Wimborne was to be fairly easily persuaded into the sale of the company. What to him may have seemed an overwhelming responsibility, was to the Midland businessman Arthur Keen a necessary element in his dream of integrating not only the making of steel and its primary products, such as rails and billets, but also the manufacture of finished articles such as wire, screws, nails and the myriad other fasteners which were so vital to the engineering industry, and in which he had already made his name.

ARTHUR KEEN

This man, who more than anyone else could claim to be the architect of Guest, Keen and Nettlefolds, was not an engineer. But he worked for a time as a railway goods agent at Smethwick, where he became acquainted with many of the Black Country businessmen who had made money out of the small engineering undertakings for which the region was famous. He married the daughter of one of the richest, and was funded by his father-in-law when he set up in partnership with one Francis Watkins, who possessed the British rights to an American patent nut-making machine. Such was the expanding market for all kinds of fasteners (nuts and bolts) that the company grew rapidly, the patent having given them an edge over their competitors. Within ten years it was floated as the Patent Nut & Bolt Co, and proceeded to go from strength to strength, taking over Weston & Grice in 1865. This was important because this company not only manufactured a wide variety of railway fasteners, for which there seemed to be an insatiable demand, but also possessed an ironworks, foundry and coal mines at Cwmbran. Thus the PNB had access to its own ironmaking facility, though a dated one.

In the meantime Arthur Keen was establishing himself as one of the most

Arthur Keen

powerful of Midlands businessmen. He was quick to take advantage of every business opportunity that arose, buying and selling patents, particularly for machinery, and integrating the undertaking as far as possible. It soon became apparent, however, that the demand was for steel, rather than wrought iron products, and it was eventually decided in the 1890's to lay down a steelworks at Cwmbran. One of the people consulted by Keen as to the efficacy of the design was E P Martin, the Dowlais manager, and it was almost certainly through him that Keen learnt that Lord Wimborne might be willing to sell a business which was not only a thriving concern, but which included an up-to-date steelworks at Cardiff. Acquisition of such a company would, he told his shareholders in 1899, "give the company a position of complete independence; to enable it to hold its own in competition with the whole world."

By 1898 there were strong rumours that the Dowlais Iron company was about to be sold, and these were confirmed in the following year when a limited company was formed to take over Lord Wimborne's industrial properties, so that they could be separately valued. In 1900 negotiations with Arthur Keen were successfully completed, and the new company of Guest, Keen & Co was formed to take over both Keen's existing Patent Nut & Bolt Company, and the former Dowlais Iron Company.

The creation of this company seems to have whetted Arthur Keen's appetite for further mergers, and he did not have to look far. Just across the road from Keen's Smethwick headquarters were the works of the most successful British manufacturers of woodscrews – Nettlefolds.

NETTLEFOLDS

It is now necessary to retreat even further back into the nineteenth century. In 1823 John Sutton Nettlefold was a wholesale ironmonger in London. Three years later he purchased a French patent which enabled him to set up a small water-

*John Sutton
Nettlefold*

powered factory in Sunbury, where he made woodscrews to a variety of specifications. So successful was this enterprise that a few years later he opened a steam-powered factory in Birmingham, the centre of the wood screw trade. In 1851 he visited the Great Exhibition, where he may well have been impressed with the idea of automatic screwmaking, for in 1854 he bought an American patent for making pointed screws using automatic lathes. This was a far-sighted move, but it needed capital, not only for the patent but also for building yet another factory to house the new machinery. This capital was to be provided by Nettlefold's brother-in-law, Joseph Chamberlain, grandfather of the future prime minister and himself a well-known politician in his own right. Thus was born Nettlefold and Chamberlain, the firm which dominated screw-manufacture in Britain for the next twenty years.

The new factory was the largest in the Midlands, yet by the 1870s the firm had acquired three more, including their first wire-drawing mill, which they called the Imperial Wire Company. Management of the firm had passed to the sons of the original partners, and when the Chamberlains eventually sold out in 1874, they left a company of world stature, well able to fight off competition both at home and abroad. Indeed, the public flotation of Nettlefolds Ltd in 1880 was occasioned by the need to finance expansion. This included the takeover of the Manchester Steel Screw Company, a significant move because it convinced J H Nettlefold, then Managing Director, that steel wire could be made of the uniform quality necessary for woodscrew manufacture. Up till then the screws were made from wire drawn from high quality bar iron.

THE FIRST CASTLE WORKS

Some time in the 1860s Nettlefold and Chamberlain had acquired land at Hadley, near Wellington. Here they established an iron works which included a blast furnace, puddling furnaces, and rolling mills to convert the bar iron to the

high quality coil needed for woodscrews. The mock turret in a nearby field not only gave a name to the works, which became the Castle Iron Co, but also gave a trademark to the company.

It was at this works J H Nettlefold decided to experiment with steelmaking, and a small Bessemer plant was erected there under the guidance of Edward Steer. There had been considerable reluctance to invest in steel, because to replace wrought iron throughout the whole of the screwmaking process would be extremely costly, but eventually it was recognised that the superior qualities of steel were going to make such a transformation inevitable. A small steel plant was not cost-effective, however. What was needed was a new, larger works, close to a supply of pig iron and with good communications.

Edward Steer was duly dispatched to South Wales, where he settled on a site at Rogerstone, a village in the Ebbw Valley. Here there was an excellent water supply, rail connections with the valley collieries and the Midlands, and easy access to Newport docks.

CASTLE WORKS, ROGERSTONE

Once again it is necessary to look back, for this was not the first iron works at Rogerstone. At the end of the eighteenth century there had been a forge there. Two mills, one powered by water and the other by steam, rolled bars which were sent first of all in horse-drawn carts and then along a tram road to a tinplate works at Tydu. In 1806 the Tydu estate was for sale, and was advertised in glowing terms:

> The country is highly picturesque, remarkable for rich and diversified scenery...The newly-erected works which are well adapted for tin plate or hoop mills have a constant supply of water from the river Ebbw so as to work in the dryest weather...

The machinery consists of a cast iron water wheel, 16 feet in diameter and 12 feet wide, with counter shaft and fly wheel 20 feet in diameter, iron shears, two sets of wrought iron pillars and boxes, and two slitting furnaces. Upon the opposite side is a counter shaft and a clog wheel with two bloom furnaces for rolling bar iron.

Sadly, when the iron foundry was again put up for sale in 1845, it was by now in a "dilapidated condition". However the census of 1841 refers to many ironworkers in Rogerstone, among them rollers and iron refiners. The rollers could earn an amazing seventy shillings a week when trade was brisk, ten times as much as a farm labourer. But the oldfashioned iron and tin plate works at Rogerstone and Tydu could not compete with the big ironworks, particularly when the transition to steel began. In 1879 the Rogerstone works closed, to be followed a year later by those at Tydu.

The valley was desolate, as a contemporary poem relates:

All is silent, dark and dismal,
Something like a prison cell,
Not the sound of any signal,
Neither whistle, nor a bell.
Every home is out of order
In depression very deep;
On the banks of Ebbw river
Every willow seems to weep.

Not surprisingly the arrival of Nettlefolds at Rogerstone was greeted with considerable enthusiasm. In 1886 Edward Steer moved down to Rogerstone, to take up residence in a house specially built for him, so that he could oversee the building of the new works. These were to consist of an acid Bessemer plant at

Edward Steer

Rogerstone, charged with pig iron imported through Newport docks. Also at Rogerstone were the rolling mills, while a hoop mill, which was extended three years later, was laid down at Tydu.

Edward Steer was not the only person to move from Shropshire – hundreds of workers from Hadley's Castle Works came to Rogerstone. Eric Osment recalls how his grandfather, George Hampton, walked all the way with his young son, while his wife and daughters came on the train. "There were gangs of them came down. They walked in batches of about twenty. They didn't stay anywhere, just slept rough on the roadside. They didn't have much money, see, just enough for the food to get them here." Indeed, so great was the influx of "Shroppies" that the

Part of Castle Works, Rogerstone, before the First World War, showing clearly the rural nature of the site.

Rogerstone House Property and Investment Company was founded in order to build houses for them. The new development included Charles, Edwin and James Street, which all led off the main road, as well as the Rogerstone Hotel and some shops. George Hampton had been a builder in the Hadley Castle works, and he now worked under Charles Martin, who not only built houses for the workers, but the steelworks as well. "Charlie Martin built the blast engine house, and the chimney stacks, and the viaduct – he was the king pin. He built his own house, the lovely big red building by the chapel. He built that, too, for all the Methodists."

Much smaller two-bedroomed houses for the less well off were built around St John's Square, which made up the Nook, as it was called. The name presumably reflected the closeness of the little community, whose Shropshire connections were reflected in the street names (Hadley and Wellington). There were no gardens, but communal clothes-lines stretched across the square. Like many groups of immigrant workers the "Shroppies" gained a reputation for drinking and fighting: "They were big hitters – always liked to get the first one in." They were doubtless resented by the locals, because they got the best jobs; "They had the knowhow, didn't they, so of course they were the rollers and got the most money." Every Whitsun, however, a truce was called and a Procession of Witness, consisting of worshippers, Sunday School scholars and teachers from the Church and all the chapels in the neighbourhood would assemble in St John's Square to be addressed by the curate and the pastors.

It was the establishment of Castle Works in Rogerstone that established Nettlefolds as the neighbour of the new giant, Guest Keen & Co, not only in Birmingham but also in South Wales.

THE FORMATION OF GUEST, KEEN AND NETTLEFOLDS

Arthur Keen had shown interest in a link with the thriving Nettlefolds company in the past, and although its directors were not enthusiastic, they were eventually persuaded into a merger by the fear that the PNB might otherwise start competing in the woodscrew market. It was also hoped, vainly as it turned out, that the pig iron and steel produced at Dowlais and Dowlais Cardiff would be suitable for woodscrew manufacture. Some of the Nettlefolds directors, including Edward Nettlefold and Edward Steer, became directors of the new company, and thus in 1902 was born one of the great engineering enterprises of the twentieth century – Guest, Keen and Nettlefolds.

Arthur Keen's dream in creating this company was to integrate the manufacture of steel goods. The company's own blast furnaces would be charged with ore and coal from its own mines, and the pig iron thus obtained would go to charge the company's steelworks. From there billets could be rolled into whatever form the customer required, or they could be transported to other company plant for fashioning into finished products.

The interests of Guest, Keen and Nettlefold were to extend far beyond South Wales, and its history, which has been ably related elsewhere, is correspondingly complex. The purpose of this narrative from now on is to show how the traditions of the heavy side of the industry, long ago established on Dowlais Top and now being carried on in Cardiff, were to combine with the different traditions of the light side, which were developing in South Wales at Rogerstone and Coverack Road, Newport.

THE HEAVY SIDE – DOWLAIS AND CARDIFF

Arthur Keen may have achieved his ambition, but the future development of the steelmaking elements of his integrated company was not without difficulty. Once again there were reservations about the viability of the original Dowlais works in Merthyr, and once again closure, however attractive a proposition commercially, was rejected as being too damaging to the local community. Instead a programme of modernisation was embarked upon: new blast furnaces were installed and rail-rolling capacity was increased. Moreover the acquisition by GKN of the once great Cyfarthfa Works, now faltering under the same forces that threatened Dowlais, to some extent eased the pressure, since it was clear that in the event of a need for closure Cyfarthfa would be (and indeed was) sacrificed before Dowlais. Morale was further raised in 1912 when King George V and Queen Mary visited the works and lunched at Dowlais House. Spectacular arches, one of coal and one of steel, were erected to mark the occasion.

Undoubtedly the managers of the steelmaking side of GKN, both in Cardiff and Dowlais, found that things had changed. Instead of being independent, they were now partners in a large enterprise whose interests always had to be considered first. What was more, the integration that Keen had hoped for did not progress smoothly: steel made from Dowlais pig iron contained too much phosphorus and sulphur to be suitable for wire-drawing, and this meant that high quality ore had to be specially purchased from Westmorland in order to

This picture shows the King and Queen leaving Dowlais Works through the 'steel arch' which was especially constructed for their visit.

Dowlais House decorated to receive the royal visit. This picture clearly shows how near the house was to the works.

meet Nettlefolds' requirements. This reduced the need for Spanish ore, and also disrupted long-established manufacturing processes.

Despite these difficulties Dowlais-Cardiff remained steadily profitable throughout the first decade of the century, and, being geared to produce plate for ship-building, benefited from the naval rearmament which preceded the First World War. By 1912 the general manager was writing to Arthur Keen about "the heavy demand for plate and the tonnage we have on our books for delivery." As well as the Admiralty, customers included Harland and Wolff, Vickers, and Cammell-Laird.

THE FIRST WORLD WAR AND AFTER

Needless to say, the First World War itself greatly increased the demand for steel products, both for shipbuilding and armour-plating, and also for artillery and shells. The very nature of this particular conflict involved a great deal of heavy bombardment, and it took place at a time when patriotism dictated an acceptance of horrendous human loss and thus prolonged the slaughter. Steelmakers benefited from government investment in new plant and technical advances, and from consequent increase in funds. But they suffered, too, not only from the death or disablement of many skilled workers and young managers (fifty were lost from Rogerstone alone) but also from the disruption and distortion of manufacturing processes.

But perhaps the worst legacy of the war was the economic chaos that followed. The post-war boom, which was perhaps to be expected, was followed by collapse, which was not. Cyfarthfa Works shut down for ever, and when steel prices fell sharply the plate mill at East Moors also closed, albeit temporarily. This was not merely a local problem, since in the steel industry as a whole a third of the workforce was made redundant. Nevertheless it was clear that in Cardiff and Dowlais one of the main stumbling blocks to progress was the half share in the Orconera Iron Company. This obliged them to continue with acid steelmaking long after most other works, which used basic technology, were able to take advantage of local high phosphorus ores.

Though productivity picked up spasmodically it was gradually becoming apparent that the decline in the staple industries of the nineteenth century, on which the industrial revolution had been based, was irreversible. The lurch from recession to slump was reflected in the fact that by August 1928 only one blast furnace was in operation in Dowlais-Cardiff, and the steelworks was working at half capacity. In Merthyr the situation was even more desperate; there were no UK orders for rails, and a consignment of Egyptian rails proved unsatisfactory. In 1929 a company report doubted the economic viability of either steelworks, suffering as they were from fluctuating orders and outdated technology.

The desperation of the GKN board can be gauged from the alacrity with which they responded to an approach from their local rival, Sir Charles Wright,

This picture, taken in about 1916, shows cranes discharging ore in Roath Dock while rails are piled awaiting shipment.

chairman of Baldwins, steelmakers with works in Margam and Port Talbot. He proposed a merger of the heavy steel interests of the two companies, which would remove competition and increase opportunities for rationalisation and capital investment. Within three days agreement was reached, and by February the new enterprise was launched as the British (Guest, Keen, Baldwins) Iron & Steel Company.

This was a death knell for the works at Dowlais. GKB lacked the nostalgic links which had saved it from closure in the late nineteenth century, and despite

The dominance of Merthyr by the Dowlais Works can clearly be seen here.

efforts to gain orders the new enterprise decided that Dowlais would close. It was the low point of the depression – three thousand jobs were lost and five years later a government commission reported that two thirds of the insurable population of Merthyr were unemployed. The works which were founded by the Guests lay derelict, as a kind of awful memorial, until after the Second World War, and now, except for the stables, nothing remains at all – not even Dowlais House.

Dowlais Works stands bleak and derelict, April 1935.

In Cardiff things at first did not seem much better. In 1930 only one blast furnace was in operation, and the manufacture of plate had been transferred to Port Talbot. For the first couple of years of the decade the continuing slump militated against any plans for the future, and, though ironmaking continued, the outlook for steel looked bleak. Things looked up in 1933, however, and approaches were made to the Bankers Industrial Development Company, which, as its name suggests, had been formed with a view to enabling the banks to assist in industrial re-organisation. In the end the BIDT agreed to support the rebuilding of the steelworks, on condition that GKN confirmed their intention of laying down a continuous rod mill next to the site, thus providing an instant

Unemployed men among the dereliction of Dowlais Works in the 1930's.

market. GKN, which had been quite happy to rid itself of the capital-intensive heavy side of its operations, was, as we shall see, only too willing to re-locate the by now flagging Castle Works to a Cardiff site.

CASTLE WORKS AGAIN

At first the steelworks at Rogerstone flourished. One of the first managers was John Williams, who moved from Shropshire to live in the big house next to the works. He was "a tall, corpulent, good-humoured man" according to Edgar Brown, and he retired at the turn of the century, to be succeeded by his son. By then the works contained two Bessemer converters, as well as a variety of rolling mills which included an entirely new semi-continuous rod mill. Edgar Brown, whose family had moved to Rogerstone in the 1890s, records how "it took some time to get used to the place being brilliantly lit up by the works at night, the sparks flying up like fireworks." This was a great boon in the days before streetlights: Eric Osment's mother, who lived in Rogerstone, used to come home from courting his father in Bassaleg by the light of the Bessemer furnace. "She'd wait for them to tap the furnace, and then you could read a paper, it was as light as day, and they'd all bolt across the fields to get home."

John Williams senior

Such was the early success of Rogerstone that in 1901 Nettlefolds decided to close two wire-drawing mills in Birmingham, and to open Imperial Mills at Coverack Road, Newport, close to the docks. The South Wales Argus of 1902 reported that "the entire Works as regards machinery and fittings, are a splendid specimen of the best and most modern type". There would be "a couple of the most powerful gas engines to be found in this part of the world", and the writer trusted that "for the sake of Newport" the works would become world-famous. From now on, steel rod was sent by train from Rogerstone to Newport to be drawn into the appropriate wire for the various fasteners which were still made in Birmingham.

Inside the wire mill at Coverack Road in the 1930's.

THE NAIL FACTORY

Among the mills installed at Rogerstone had been one for the rolling of the concave strip necessary for the manufacture of Hugget's Patent Horse Nails, which were at the time produced in Birmingham. It was this H P Wire Nail Works which was moved to Tydu, and linked to the main works by a private railway. Once more there were immigrants; this time nailmakers from Birmingham who came to set up the machines. Bill Redding, who started work in the nail factory in 1917, remembers: "The main men there, who understood the job, were all from Birmingham. They'd come down to start the place up, because nobody knew anything about it, locally. There were about seven setters, and the head toolmaker came with them." It was a different world; the manager of the factory had a pony and trap, and the young Bill Redding used to go into Newport with him to hold the horse, very much enjoying the ride there and back.

The nail factory at Tydu is still remembered quite clearly by people who started their working life there. It was water-powered: Arthur Bullock recalls that when he started "all the machines were run by the water wheel, the big turbine wheel fed by a dyke from the River Ebbw – about twenty foot it was, probably. There was one shaft running right the length of the factory, and belts from it that drove all the nail machines and all the machines in the toolroom." So dangerous was it that one worker was killed when his clothes got caught in one of the belts.

It was also very noisy. "They had what they called the bangers. They had wooden springs, which were pulled back and then let go to head the nails." Trevor Manley remembers: "The biggest machine would cut anything up to twelve-inch nails. You could hear the big banger, when it was running, half a mile from the factory." It was a fairly primitive place. "I started when I was fourteen, in 1932. My first job was in the tool shop, making the dies and punches, and then I went as an assistant on the machines. There was a setter and two assistants to about twelve machines. We wore overalls and aprons made from the sacks you used to put the nails into. The wire used to come from Coverack road by lorry, and if you were short of wire someone would watch the dram road for the lorry and then one of the assistants would jump on the lorry and if it had the right wire he'd sit there and make sure he got it because that would keep the machine going and they'd get a bonus.

"There were no washing facilities or proper toilets. If you went there at night you had to kick, because of the rats. And if you stopped for a meal at night, and you got together for a game of cards, when you started again you'd see the rats running from under the machines. And Mr Wellings, he was the manager and he lived in a house at the side of the nail factory, if he heard no noise coming he'd walk over in his dressing gown, and then everyone would scuttle up and get started again."

Sometimes work was short. Bill Redding grew tired of notices saying "No work during the whole of next week" and went to London for a while, but he returned after a time when he was promised regular employment. Trevor Manley was apprehensive about reporting his eighteenth birthday to the manager, because that meant a rise in wages and "sometimes they'd get rid of fellows coming up to eighteen and get younger ones back in." Once the worst of the slump was over work picked up, but by then further change was on the horizon and the nail factory was once again on the move.

GOODBYE TO ROGERSTONE

It was the First World War that was in the main responsible for the cessation of steelmaking at Rogerstone. Before then, plans had been afoot for the erection of a Siemens-Martin open-hearth furnace, and indeed, in 1914 Edward Steer and John Williams were actually in Germany inspecting the latest plant when the imminence of hostilities caused them to return hastily to Britain before making a decision. After the war was over, scrap from the battlefields of Europe provided cheap raw materials for open hearth furnaces, and in Rogerstone, as in many other places, the Bessemer process was to prove too costly in comparison. In March 1921 the last steel was made, and the billet mills eventually closed.

John Williams junior

Despite the closing of the steelworks the rolling mills had survived. Eric Osment's father was an assistant roller, and his son worked in the office of the same mill for two years. It was by now decidedly old. There was no canteen, only primitive toilets, and no drinking water laid on: "It was very hot and they all wore thick clothes, moleskin, for protection. Clogs and hand leathers too, because they'd still have to catch the red hot rods in tongs to feed them to the next rolls and they whipped them around very fast. My father's trousers were all burnt. They were all on tonnage, so they wouldn't stop, they'd work all the time except for perhaps twenty minutes for a whiff and a drink. There'd be a bucket of water hanging there but the well was four hundred yards away. They'd send the boy for that, but my father's assistant, he could drink a whole bucketful. It was murder, I can tell you."

Billets now had to be bought in from local suppliers. Later on there were plans to re-establish steelmaking at Rogerstone, but the generally poor economic climate prevented these ever coming to fruition. John Williams was not without ideas, but the GKN board was perhaps cautious about investing heavily in Rogerstone when there were serious problems elsewhere in the company.

In the early 1930's there was a short period of revival. In part this reflected a general improvement in trading conditions, but it was also connected with the arrival of Roland Harding as manager in 1930. He was a man in a hurry – according to Edgar Brown he "tried to be the engine driver and the engine simultaneously." He cannot have been easy to work with, but his determination to succeed resulted in a reorganisation of the nail factory, together with the purchase of new machines from the continent. Bill Redding remembers being impressed by the first of the new German nail machines: " With no exaggeration they fixed it to the floor and I had a look, and pulled the wheel round and watched it work. All I had to do was to find out what thickness of wire was needed, press the button, and off she went like a house on fire. The nails were perfect, beautiful nails." At the same time Harding installed a wire-drawing machine at Tydu so that rod did not have to be sent from Rogerstone to Coverack Road to be drawn, and then transported back again to be made into nails. A measure of his success is that under his management nail production increased tenfold.

Nail machine.

GUEST, KEEN & NETTLEFOLDS, LIMITED

GENERAL VIEW

THE STEEL MILLS, NEWPORT, MON.

BILLET BANK & TRANSPORTER

LOADING DECK

STEEL HOOP MILLS

WIRE ROD MILL

WORKS AT ROGERSTONE & NEWPORT (MON.)

AND ASSOCIATED COMPANIES.

*Another page from
the GKN booklet
shows activities in
Newport and
Rogerstone in the
1920's*

However nothing could disguise the fact that the rod mills at Rogerstone were outdated and when this was combined with the knowledge that plans were under way to rebuild the Dowlais-Cardiff Works, the future of Castle works at Rogerstone was indeed questionable. In 1933 Harding was asked by the board of GKN "to prepare a report generally on the policy to be adopted...whether the works remained at Rogerstone or were transferred to Cardiff." His conclusion must have been inescapable – with new opportunities presenting themselves at Cardiff it would make commercial sense to construct a modern rod mill close to the new steelworks. It was then likely that the rest of the Rogerstone operations , as well as the wiredrawing at Newport, would gradually follow.

The news of the impending move to Cardiff was generally greeted with resignation, if not enthusiasm by the Rogerstone workers. Many of them, after all, had family traditions of moving to be where the work was, and in any case the company was eager that their skills would not be lost. A special bus service was provided for each shift, and although some of the younger men moved to Cardiff, others chose to travel daily, either on the buses or by bicycle. Trevor Manley recalls: "It was a bit of an upheaval at the time of course, but they laid on the buses, which you got used to. There were special bus stops, which made it handy for the men to get on. I always got on at Rogerstone church, which wasn't a hundred yards from where I lived." The local effects of the closing of the works were in any case offset by the fact that the site was sold to the Northern Aluminium Company, who have been smelting aluminium there ever since.

PART THREE: STEELMAKING THRIVES

The late 1930s, therefore, were to see the establishment in Cardiff of the latest in steelmaking technology, not only in the primary production of steel itself, but also in the secondary manufacture of rod, wire and nails. Though GKB and GKN were to be run as separate enterprises, they were nevertheless to a large extent dependent upon each other. While they flourished the whole area around Roath and East docks reverberated with all the noise, glare and bustle associated with the traditions of steel manufacture. Although in the interwar years there had been a significant decline in the old industries it was by no means accepted, particularly by working people, that this was either inevitable or permanent. Therefore the revitalising of Cardiff steelmaking was seen as an indication that the economic tribulations of the thirties were at last at an end, and that with what amounted to brand new works the future could only be bright. Many people remember these times, and from now on their testimony forms an important element in the story.

EAST MOORS

The rebuilt works at East Moors was to combine, like its predecessors, the production of iron and steel. As far as iron was concerned, two of the existing blast furnaces had been rebuilt, and were considered to be capable of supplying sufficient molten metal for the steelmaking process. The third and older furnace was to supply pig iron for other South Wales steelworks. Gas from the furnaces was used to heat new coke ovens, which in turn supplied gas for the steelmaking processes. Any surplus was sold to supplement Cardiff's town gas supply, and slag from the furnaces was converted into tarmac for road building.

The new steelworks was designed by J S Hollings, and he also superintended its construction. Steel was to be made, at last using basic technology, in two open

Steelmaking at East Moors. The picture shows molten iron being tipped from a ladle into the open hearth furnance on the right. The ladle operator can be seen in the top left hand corner.

hearth and three tilting furnaces. These were so-called because, instead of tap-holes in the furnace wall having to be knocked out when conversion to steel was complete, they could be tilted and tapped in the manner of a teapot. Molten steel from either process was poured into cast iron ingot moulds, which were stripped away when the metal solidified. The ingots, though still hot, were then reheated still further and conveyed to the cogging mill, where they were rolled into blooms which in turn went to the new Morgan continuous mill for yet more rolling into billets or slabs. A new Lamberton mill was installed to roll lighter sections, such as rails and colliery arches.

Heavy though this side of the industry still was, it is interesting to see that the use of electricity had enormously lessened the size of much of the machinery, and banks of switches now replaced the huge engines which had been installed at the end of the nineteenth century. The works was now one of the most modern in Europe, and indeed so much steel was produced that a fourth blast furnace was built. Overproduction might well have resulted in another economic depression, but once again war was looming so that contracts for rearmament increased demand.

CASTLE WORKS, CARDIFF

In the event GKN's continuous rod mill started production before the new steel works. This mill, like the billet mill at the steelworks, was built by the American Morgan company, but its specifications, and the designs for the site, had been drawn up by the young George Phipps. It was one of the first rod mills in which the rod was guided automatically, instead of by hand, from one set of rolls to the next. Robert Gwynne, who lived in Splott, got a job laying down the new rod mill, and as soon as it started he went for a job there. "First of all I was a charger, loading billets into the furnace, and then I got moved onto the toggle shears, which cut the rough ends off the red hot billets as they came out of the furnace before going into the roughing train."

Many of the rollermen who had worked in the Rogerstone rod mill moved to operate this one; this was not surprising, because their status was high and their skills were valuable to the company. A "cobble" (when the rolled steel goes out of control) could be avoided through fast thinking and skill, as a colleague recalls: "Those Rogerstone boys knew how to use a pair of tongs. Many a time I wondered at Bilter Davies as he caught the front end of a scrap rod as it flashed across a repeater and led it straight into the mouth of the scrap gobbler to be coiled and returned to the steel works in East Moors."

May 1935 – the new Cardiff rod mill under construction, with the cranes of Roath Dock in the background.

Robert Gwynne was on Bilter Davies' shift: "I was afraid at first. They were all one family, all intermarried with each other, but it was great."

At first there was a problem with steel supply, as the neighbouring steelworks was not yet in operation, but once the first billets were rolled in January 1936 it was clear that the relocation was fully justified. The long-expected decision to move both the wire-drawing operation from Coverack Road and the nail factory from Tydu was then quickly taken. As in the case of the rod mill, many of the workers moved with them, many travelling to Cardiff daily. Fred Roberts, who worked as a fitter preparing the coils of wire for despatch, was not pleased. "I lived in a little village then, and I was travelling four miles to work, and now it was sixteen miles." Ivor West, who worked in the office, reckoned that the move was worth it. The new wire-drawing mill in Cardiff was "the number one unit in the whole of Europe. Basil Adams went all over the place: Italy, France, Germany, even America, and he came back with the details of all these machines. Of course they were all drawing through dies, instead of plates, and the machines went much faster. So at Cardiff we were producing a lot more wire with the same number of people. But there weren't the same skills, because at Coverack Road you had to be an apprentice and learn to make your own plates and your own tools. At Cardiff it was more watching machines."

Bill Redding was impressed by the new nail factory. "It was a nice big place and a nice high roof." Wire was now drawn on the premises, as Trevor Manley recalls: "It was a lot easier in more ways than one. The nails were moved about better, and the wire was brought up from the wire department on trolleys. That sometimes caused a bit of bother because they couldn't get the wire through as quickly as we wanted it. Then you'd go down to and wait by the machine down at the wire-drawing and you'd bring it up on the trolley yourself." So efficient were the new German machines that, under the managership of the young Bob Spary, they once made a thousand tons of nails in a week. This was partly accidental, according to Bill Redding. "The orders were calling for heavy work, and the machines were pounding away, and in the office someone was saying it was 900 ton, so we put some of the machines on the biggest stuff they would cut and they did it." Bob Spary was delighted, but remembered that in the determination to reach the target the nippings had clogged up the machines.

Further investment was made in the laying down of a combined merchant bar and strip mill, and in the establishment of a cold rolling plant and the building of new offices. Frank Perks was very pleased: he moved from Rogerstone to be a clerk in the bar mill in Cardiff. "All of us in our office, we all went to Cardiff. My job then was to keep records of everything that was rolled. I had a brand new office with a proper flush toilet and everything. Before the war my boss had a car and he'd give three of us a lift to work with him, but then we'd have to wait for him to finish after everyone else had gone home."

Castle Works was linked by rail to the steelworks and to Roath Dock, as well as to the main railway line. Most of its development at Cardiff took place during the course of 1938, with a gratifying increase in output to match it. Within a year, however, war had again intervened to disrupt normal business activity.

The main gate of Castle Works in 1936. The gatehouse on the left is still standing but the main offices, visible through the gates, have been demolished and replaced by gardens. The castle emblems have been rescued; one is with ASW and the other in the Welsh Industrial and Maritime Museum.

Rows of machines in the nail factory.

THE SECOND WORLD WAR

Steelmaking in Cardiff benefited very little from the war. Steel was needed for armaments, but this served mostly to disrupt normal production. Arches were made for air raid shelters, sections for Bailey bridges, and specialised shell and structural steels were produced for armaments. The requirements of the Ministry of Supply severely restricted free decision making – co-operation in the war effort replaced competition in the open market. Investment in increased capacity certainly attracted government money, though Excess Profit Tax prevented the accumulation of extra funds. The possibility of bombing necessitated blackout precautions at East Moors, which involved the roofing in of several previously open-air processes. In the event the Cardiff Docks area escaped the really heavy bombing experienced by Plymouth, Liverpool or even Swansea, but the disruption was there and many people have vivid memories of the war years.

Ronny Knox remembers his father, who was a security officer, working as a roof spotter. "His job was to stay up in a little box on top of the general offices and if there was an imminent danger warning they would tell the firm and they would decide who was to go to the shelters. They'd still keep the mill rolling but if my father thought it was dangerous he'd give a signal and they'd shut the mills down." Stan Carpenter went up there as a volunteer. "I was up there in the first bad blitz we had, in this little cubbyhole, only a little brick shelter. It was a hell of an air raid that night and I could see over towards Grangetown and there were fires there." Inside the mill was not much better. "If there was an air raid the roller was supposed to stay at his station and see the steel through so it didn't go flying off everywhere. Once we were up in the mill itself and you either had to go outside to the shelter and risk breaking your neck in the pitch dark or come through the mill and take the risk of steel flying."

Air raid shelter.

On Jack Bond's first day in the nail factory a land mine was dropped on it. "I went to work the next morning and all we could do was sweep. There was glass everywhere, piles of glass all through the factory." Bill Redding was there when it happened. "All of a sudden there was a boom, and the blast shifted the roof, and years of dust and soot and soap came down. We couldn't see, it was terrible." He also had to do guard duty, but didn't think much of it. "When the alarm went I was supposed to run and pick up a rifle and run to a pillar box and there was supposed to be an air raid warden in the pillar box and a home guard. But sometimes you'd be in there hours and no sign of a warden and the all clear would go and you'd say "ah,well," and put the rifle back. It wasn't much satisfaction sitting by yourself with the guns going off all about you." John Benson, who worked in the rod mill, was also on guard duty. "We used to have gun places all over the works. But the comical part was we were given five bullets, and if you wanted to shoot you had to phone up to get permission, so by the time you had permission you'd be dead."

For the people travelling to Rogerstone the journey could be hazardous. Frank Perks used to cycle to Cardiff in the summer . "I remember, on one occasion I was on my own, and it was in the day time, and I was in Forge Lane. And there was a German plane overhead and ack ack guns were firing and I carried on riding my bicycle until suddenly I heard 'ping, ping' all around. What it was, was the shrapnel from the guns, so I got off the bike immediately and went and stood by the wall to avoid it. Another time at night, on the bicycle again, I couldn't go down the road because a bomb had dropped there." Bill Redding had similar experiences. "I'd get off the bus and be walking along home, in the dark, with no hat on or anything, and on the road there would be sparks flying up wherever the shrapnel was hitting the road before me, and I just kept going because you didn't know where it was going to fall next." Ivor West remembers going home through Newport one night "and there was a whole formation of German bombers at so

Members of Castle Works staff who undertook fire service and air raid security work during the war.

little height you could see into their cockpits. They knew they were coming and started firing at them. They used to come to Newport and follow the river."

Many of the work force were called up, some never to return, or to seek different jobs when they came back. Others were turned down for the forces on the grounds that they were in an essential industry. On the whole those who returned found either their old jobs waiting for them, or new opportunities in different departments.

A general view of Castle Works in the late 1940's.

AFTER THE WAR

As far as steelmaking in Cardiff was concerned, the most significant factor in the years following the war was not the aftermath of the war itself, but the election of a Labour government committed to the nationalisation of the steel industry. How much of the industry would be nationalised was not clear, and in the hope that steel trading operations might be exempt Castle Works became part of the newly-incorporated GKN (South Wales) Ltd; a similar company was created for the Midlands operations. At the same time the formation of the Steel Company of Wales, to which GKB sold the Margam and Port Talbot Works, isolated East Moors as the primary producer of steel in Cardiff.

Steel nationalisation proved to be a complex and controversial issue, however, so that its implementation was delayed until after the election of the second Labour government in 1950. In the meantime there was a huge demand for steel both at home and for export, with the result that even with the possibility of nationalisation hanging over them the steel companies were prepared to expand and modernise.

THE ROLLING MILLS

In 1950 a new continuous rod mill was laid down at a recently acquired site in Tremorfa. John Benson was one of those who helped set up the new mill; by now he was an assistant rougher and joining the elite of the shift. "I spent half my life trying to get there and in the end I did." Indeed, by the time he retired he was a roller man "who was responsible for everything. If there were a lot of rejects then the manager would argue with him and he'd sort it out with the men. But on the whole it didn't work a lot like that because we all worked together." Nevertheless, "Basically speaking the roller man was in charge. Even the mill manager wouldn't actually order the roller man about: he was the man, if you understand what I mean." Jim Ashford, from the bar and strip mill, agreed. "The roller man was responsible in every way. Everybody looked up to the roller man."

In the days when shifts competed for bonuses the individual roller man's knowledge and experience were his greatest assets, for his shift's bonus depended on his ability to keep the mill rolling and the number of cobbles to a minimum. There was little specific training and knowledge was handed down and jealously guarded. The roller man's most valuable possession was his "little black book" in which he recorded the roll-settings which produced the best results, and which was shown to nobody, least of all to fellow workers or to managers. "I wouldn't let any one else see my book," said John Benson. "I kept all my secrets in there." Jim Ashford recalls Ernie Gill, a manager, approaching a furnaceman. "And he wanted to know something and the furnaceman

The roughing stand at Cardiff rod mill. As the steel billets pass through the pairs of rolls they get thinner and so have to travel faster. On the right is the loop or repeater around which the rod travels before passing through the sets of rolls that make up the finishing train. The rollermen's assistants were in charge of different parts of the operation: roughing, finishing and so on.

wouldn't tell him. He said "No. If I tell you, you'll know as much as me and my job won't be so secure. And you know, unfortunately, this is what some people felt." It was Ernie Gill who made a determined effort to stamp out the "black book" system in the rod mill, but according to Robert Gwynne he had to listen to the roller men in the end. "We were making so much scrap he had to listen. In the end they had a bit of a meeting and he gave them their way and it went quite lovely then."

As part of the post-war modernisation the "small mills", which had been part of GKN's operations at Cwmbran and which rolled a wide range of specialised sections and shapes, were transferred to Tremorfa. Rather more spectacularly the original Castle Works Rod Mill was dismantled and transferred to Scunthorpe, where it eventually became a subsidiary of John Lysaght's Scunthorpe Works (thus remaining under the GKN umbrella). This was an amazingly efficient operation; dismantling started within minutes of the mill closing down on 20 December 1951, and the first rod was rolled in Scunthorpe on 11 February 1952. Men from Castle Works travelled to Scunthorpe too; some to set up the mill and then return to Cardiff, others to take their families to make a new life there.

The mill was transported in pieces on a special train. Ronny Knox was in the office then. "I consigned every little bit of material that went into every wagon." Edgar George was then a foreman fitter, and was in charge of moving the cooling unit of the mill. "I had to strip that lot down, and I had to see it actually put in a railway truck, and the railway truck was marked and linked up with other trucks and taken to Scunthorpe. And then that was transported up to Scunthorpe and some of us went up there on New Year's Day, and I had the same crew and we found the truck that our part was in. And we discharged the stuff from the truck and set it down in the new place. All that was there was an empty factory. I was up there about six weeks and then I came back."

The rod mill on the move to Scunthorpe. It travelled in sections on labelled wagons.

THE FIRST NATIONALISATION AND AFTER

Very soon after this nationalisation actually took place, and despite the defensive actions taken by the company, ownership of both GKN (South Wales) Ltd and East Moors was transferred to the Iron and Steel Confederation of Great

Britain. It was still a controversial measure, however, and when the Conservatives were returned to power only a few months later they quickly repealed it. In 1954 both companies were bought back by the parent company.

The outlook seemed good. World supplies of steel fell far short of demand, and in the next ten years approximately £5 million was spent on expanding and modernising the East Moors works, as, according to the company secretary, it

East Moors Works in May 1960 before the 'M' scheme: modernisation intended to increase output to one million tons of steel per year.

was recognised as being "one of the most efficient and economical works this side of the Atlantic." Despite the presence of contractors on the site, production was somehow maintained and there was no shutdown as there had been during the rebuild thirty years before. New offices were built, new coke ovens and sinter plant were installed, and a new system of ore handling involving kangaroo cranes was introduced. In 1961 the whole billet mill was moved to accommodate more up-to-date machinery. Tom Keen, great-grandson of Arthur Keen, had joined the company after the war as a trainee and had just become a manager. "My first real independent command was the management of the new wharf, so I became very involved with the docks and the importation of iron ore, some of which still came from Bilbao. The modernisation scheme was called the M scheme because we were supposed to bring the works up to a million ton capacity."

Meanwhile Castle Works was also modernising. In 1959 the Tremorfa rod mill was modified to increase its capacity, and two years later it was equipped with a "long loop" extension. John Benson explains: "When the red hot billets come out of the furnace they go into the roughing train, and they had increased the speed of the roughing so that they could roll nearly twice as much steel but that meant they had a loop. So then they built another finishing train so they had one roughing train feeding two finishing ones. It worked very successfully for years and years."

In 1962 a new nail factory was built at Tremorfa: some operatives moved for the third time, as did some of the machines. Nevertheless it was a new set up; indeed it was one of the most modern nail factories in the world. The machines were on plinths, and Trevor Manley thought it was noisier than ever. "It was more of a cracking noise, but you got used to it. Now there were cartons for collecting the nails, and they put them on wooden pallets for fork-lift trucks. And there was a new system for cleaning nails – well, the same principle, but you could get more in. We had our own wire-drawing department, and the wire was drawn onto steel formers which went on trucks, and when you wanted more wire you would turn on a light at the end of the row of machines and the fork truck drivers would bring it."

Lorries leaving Castle Works in 1960. The steelworks can be seen in the background.

Further additions at Tremorfa included a steel reinforcement plant, which catered for the construction industry by producing the bars necessary for reinforced concrete. In 1964 a sixteen inch section mill was installed and John Lockwood was recruited to manage it. "It was put down to roll wheel rims for lorries. It's a complicated section and very difficult to roll, because it's not symmetrical. There were about six or eight patterns. Otherwise we'd roll a large variety of sections, flats and reinforcing bars and so on." In 1971 the new TorBar department, making shaped rods for reinforced concrete was opened.

SOMERSET WIRE

In 1960 Somerset Wire arrived at Tremorfa. This company had an interesting history. In 1921 W H Berryman had set up a wire rope making factory in Bridgwater. Seventeen years later he decided to employ half a dozen operatives and to put down a wire mill to make the wire for his wire rope. Soon afterwards he was killed, and a few years later, during the war, his son was quite ready to sell the company to Kenneth Davies and Kenneth Hann, who were controlling shareholders in a much larger wire rope factory in Cardiff. They immediately offered a minority share in their business to GKN, who took the company over completely in 1950.

It was only a small company: Roy Davies worked there after the war and recalls: "There were only about twenty people working there. The wire drawers were skilled people, but they had to do everything, make plates, hammer them out and draw the wire through the plate. Production was very slow." By this time the company's potential had been recognised, because it became a pioneer in the production of wire for what was then a comparatively new building material, pre-stressed concrete. Previously there had been a problem because the stretched wire inserted into the concrete to keep it under stress tended to relax so that the surrounding concrete crumbled. Kenneth Hann devised a method of stabilizing the wire by passing an electric current through it while it was being stretched, so that the tendency to relax was greatly reduced. This was patented in 1954, and was an important breakthrough, particularly since the same process could be applied to the large-diameter strand used for bridge-building. The gain for the company was not so much in the product itself, but in the licensing of the process all over the world.

It was decided to move the heavy machinery to a new factory at Tremorfa. Edgar George was literally "in on the ground floor", since he was involved in putting down the new plant. "It was built on the tide fields, and we had to keep pumps going day and night because we were four feet below sea level. Once again I was in charge of stripping down the machines in Bridge water; they were going to leave the small ones. Anyway I went back and fore daily. It took a long time to put the factory down, and then there were problems with the stabilizer machines. Later on, if we had visitors, we had to cover the machines with tarpaulins, particularly when they came with little cameras. When we go the Queen's Award for Industry we had a big marquee and all kinds of free eats and free booze." May Wace worked there as a secretary when Somerset Wire was just establishing

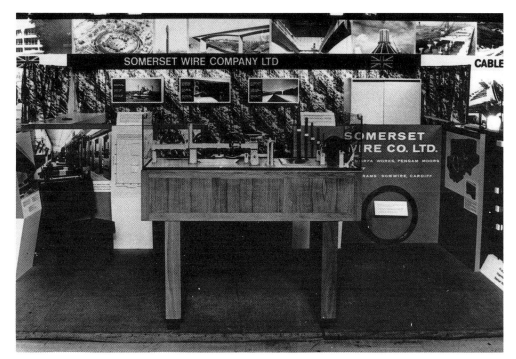

A trade stand belonging to Somerset Wire in the 1970's.

PART FOUR: STEEL IN DECLINE

From the 1960s onwards the inherent problems of primary production became harder to hide. More and more countries were producing their own steel, and at the same time the competitive spirit of steelmakers was blunted by fears of renationalisation. Problems of overmanning almost everywhere were compounded at East Moors by a failure to modernise. Years of uncertainty were followed by the gradual realisation that, although Castle Works' secondary activities might be saved, the primary production of iron and steel at East Moors could not.

PROBLEMS AT EAST MOORS

Superficially the sixties seem to have been a period of optimism, but there were ominous indications of problems ahead for East Moors, despite its recent modernisation. In the first place, it was becoming apparent that there were too many steel plants in Britain, and some would inevitably have to close. Moreover the technology of steelmaking had progressed yet again; the most modern steelworks were switching to what became known as the basic oxygen process. This in some ways resembled the Bessemer process except that instead of air being blown into the bottom of a vessel containing molten iron, pure oxygen was blown onto the top of a mixture of molten iron and scrap. The scrap was necessary to absorb the huge amount of heat given off, for the replacement of air by pure oxygen resulted in a chemical reaction which was both more violent and, significantly, even quicker than its Bessemer predecessor. Because of the speed of the process enormous amounts of steel could be produced very rapidly, and it was clear that the days of the slow open hearth furnace were numbered. Unless the new technology was installed in East Moors, therefore, in the long run the steelworks could not survive in the face of competition from more modern plant.

Adding alloys to molten steel as part of the outdated open hearth process at East Moors.

There were other problems. It had long been recognised that for an integrated steelworks the East Moors site was too small, and it was now apparent that any new scheme would have to involve a different site. As a result GKN took out options on land at Marshfield, east of Cardiff, and started to plan for a new basic oxygen works there. But this was the mid sixties and the political climate was again changing. Tom Keen remembers the mere mention of the next general election at a crucial board meeting. "There was a deathly silence and in the end the decision was taken to defer the final sanction for eighteen months. Of course, in the end Labour did get in, renationalisation did take place, and that cost Cardiff the new steel works, which is a first class example of the problems of nationalisation: it wasn't just that it was a bad thing, but that the threat of nationalisation was holding back capital investment throughout the steel industry."

The 1967 nationalisation inevitably affected the special relationship between East Moors and Castle Works. The re-rolling mills were still the major customer of the steelworks, but what was still known as "the Dowlais" was now part of the

An aerial view of East Moors in the late 1960's. The houses of Splott can be seen in the top left hand corner, and part of the Castle Works in the top right.

giant British Steel Corporation, which had much wider interests even than GKN and no particular loyalties to that company. Moreover, although the chairman of GKN was invited to be a member of the new board, he soon resigned after disagreements with Lord Melchett, the Chairman of BSC.

From the late sixties onwards there was growing apprehension about the future of East Moors, despite frequent assurances by politicians of every persuasion that it was not in doubt. Production was certainly reduced at the end of the decade, but this was seen as part of a general recession rather than the result of difficulties peculiar to Cardiff. In March 1969 Lord Melchett, Chairman of BSC, declared that there was "no need for concern" about East Moors, and in the following year James Callaghan, then MP for Cardiff West, promised "a great future for the works."

Yet there could be no escaping the fact that East Moors was old-fashioned and overmanned. Jobs had been easy to come by after the war and it was well-paid work with powerful unions locked inflexibly into national agreements. Ken Hutchings remembers how every six weeks the management had to negotiate Sunday working: "If we wanted something we'd just say no, so they'd have to give it to us or we wouldn't work." Tom Keen, as manager, was frustrated when bricklayers, quite prepared to work extra hours on the open hearth furnaces in order to increase production, could not do so because of an agreement made by their national union at the power station at Aberthaw – "because of that agreement the leaders wouldn't allow our bricklayers to do what they and we wanted." Often the overmanning was exacerbated by the unions themselves; Colin Ceshion remembers: "Very often when we went in for a rise, if we couldn't get the rise we'd try and get an extra man, which very often happened. On some jobs we needed the extra man, but on other jobs no." The result was a great deal of activity in the works which had little to do with steelmaking, as Ken

Hutchings remembers: "There were bookies in the steelworks. You could buy anything you wanted: booze, boots, clothes, cigarettes, especially at Christmas time. You could even get your hair cut."

There were whole dynasties of steelworkers, many of whom lived in Splott, an area of terraced houses dominated by the works. When the original works was built the Dowlais Iron Company had built houses in a group of streets still known as Dowlais cottages. The area was dirty and occasionally swamped with

Teeming: pouring molten steel from a ladle into ingot moulds.

sulphurous fumes. According to Ivor Harry women would look to see whether the steam from the quencher on the coke ovens was spiralling up and away or blowing towards them before doing the washing: if the wind blew in their direction everything would be covered in red dust. It was a close-knit community, bound together by its connection with "the Dowlais". Ken Hutchings was told that when his grandfather died during the war fifty-seven direct relatives had the day off to go to the funeral. "And when the war broke out the women in the Hutchings family went to work in the steel works, and that meant over sixty cousins, aunts and their wives and husbands." J J Sullivan's father had died when he was young. "But my brothers all worked in the steelworks, and they got me a job." Colin Ceshion, J J's nephew, believed when he started work there in 1951 that he was there for life. "A lot of people over there was like father and son, it was as though it would go on for ever."

STEPS TO CLOSURE

But by the beginning of the seventies crisis talks were being held which involved not only the management of BSC and East Moors, but also Callaghan and the Lord Mayor of Cardiff. For at last it was realised that for everyone except the leaders of BSC the closure of East Moors was not simply a business decision: it would have devastating effects not only on the local communities of Splott and Tremorfa, but on the city of Cardiff as a whole. In June 1971 a deputation consisting of the Lord Mayor and the three Cardiff MP's was sent to the Welsh Secretary, and within a month a civic deputation was sent to meet Monty Finniston at BSC.

Throughout this time talks of varying degrees of secrecy were taking place between all the interested parties. It was clear that without the new basic oxygen process the works could not survive, and it was equally clear that to introduce the new technology and to reduce the workforce would be an enormously expensive undertaking. Under a Conservative government not averse to private ownership, BSC would undoubtedly have been delighted for GKN to take over the plant and then modernise it: however, after two separate nationalisations GKN was understandably not prepared to go back into primary steelmaking, and indeed its chairman was more interested in light engineering than heavy steel.

GKN was, however, willing to invest further in Castle Works, and in November 1972 plans were announced for the laying down of a new rod mill on the Castle Works site in Cardiff. As the largest rod mill in the country this would

A suitably sombre view of East Moors in the 1960's.

provide a steady demand for billets from a modernised East Moors, but BSC had other plans. At the end of December, in an atmosphere of grim foreboding, Lord Melchett came to Cardiff. There was a stony meeting with the managers of East Moors, and then the long-dreaded announcement was made. The works was to close within five years, with the loss of some four thousand jobs. Despite the fact that this was no real surprise, the workforce was stunned by its brutality. Tom Keen remembers: "In the afternoon Lord Melchett was taken to meet the union leaders and they were thunderstruck. One of them asked whether the colliery arch plant would be able to go on, and he said, 'No, we're going to flatten the site.' There was complete silence. I'll never forget it."

In fact plans for the future had not been exactly finalised. The idea was that after the closure of East Moors, billets for the Cardiff operations would come partly by BSC's modernised steelworks 230 miles away at Scunthorpe and partly from a proposed new "mini-mill" – that is, a plant in which steel was made not from iron but from scrap, melted by means of the heat from an electric arc. The molten steel would then be continuously cast into billets, rather than ingots. The mini-mill would therefore eliminate not only primary ironmaking in blast furnaces, but also the various processes involved in the making of billets from ingots. Far from employing thousands, there would be at most five hundred jobs.

The now doomed colliery arch plant.

It was not clear who was going to build the mini-mill, and in any case the workforce was not prepared meekly to accept closure. The steelworkers had many supporters who were prepared to question the practicability of reliance on the output of BSC's steelworks at Scunthorpe, since it would have to import ore through Immingham, and billets would have to be sent by train to Cardiff along what was scarcely a direct route. There was even some doubt about the capacity of the steelworks themselves, since BSC had also announced the erection of its own new rod mill nearby.

In the early months of 1973, therefore, an official campaign to save East Moors was launched, with the backing of the City Council. A fighting fund was set up, and a special campaign bus was acquired. MP's were lobbied and steelworkers all over the country were asked to support East Moors. Ken Hutchings led the campaign but admits now: "We travelled all over the country and spoke to almost every cabinet minister of both parties while they were in power; we had meetings with Harold Wilson, Heath, Callaghan. But those of us in the know realised that the campaign was only to continue the steelworks until we could get some other industry and in order to negotiate a better payment of redundancy."

Ironically the works itself was still profitable – in April 1973 it was announced that it had had the best operating month in its history, and had broken many production records in the previous year. In July George Thomas, then MP for Cardiff East declared that "Cardiff is fighting for its life."

From all this GKN stood aloof. Threats by the steelworkers to ban deliveries to GKN works in Cardiff were called off when it was pointed out that depriving the GKN workers of their jobs would not solve the problems of East Moors. Members of steel unions who worked at GKN marched in support of their East Moors brothers, but in August 1973 GKN announced that it was indeed going to build the mini-mill, on the Tremorfa site. It was clear that the company was prudently making sure of its own supplies of billets, and it rendered the survival of East Moors impossible. It was, however, a significant decision for the future of steelmaking in Cardiff, because it was on the basis of this combination of a modern steelworks and up-to-date rodmill that the future Allied Steel and Wire was to build its success.

Workers outside the campaign bus which took them to London to lobby MPs.

Still the fight went on, but with every month it was clear that the workforce was more dispirited. There was open talk of compensation terms, and an air of resignation was gradually spreading. However, in response to the campaign Lord

Beswick had been commissioned by the government to inquire into the proposed steel closures, and when it was announced in July that the works had turned in an annual profit of £3 million spirits rose again. In February 1975, as a result of Beswick's steel review, reprieve was granted for four years: the works was not to close before January 1980. But, although "a bright future" was predicted for the works, in October its managing director, Tom Keen, left to go to GKN. This was significant because he was known to be steadfast in his resistance to closure, and his departure was seen as a demonstration that BSC was determined to press ahead.

In the end it was not the departure of Tom Keen, nor even the opening of the new Castle Works rodmill and the starting up of Tremorfa Steel Works that was to accelerate the closure of East Moors; it was the economy. By the start of 1976 steelworkers all over South Wales were being laid off. In the summer production was falling, and although during the winter over £1 million was spent on maintenance there were few who now truly believed that the works could be saved. "In the last twelve months there were people doing nothing", Ken Hutchings remembers. By the summer of 1977 the unions were offering to co-operate in slimming down the workforce, and redundancy packages were negotiated. City councillors started to advocate acceptance of the inevitability of closure and to press for job creation. By the autumn the international crisis in steel was serious enough for most workers to accept early closure if the pay-off was high enough, and after Christmas there was a steady trickle of national trade union leaders to the works, clearly to discuss redundancy terms.

This was not like the winter of 1972. There could be no hope of long-term survival; the opportunities for modernisation had long since passed; the works was not running at full capacity and morale was low. When the announcement finally came in the small hours of March 9th 1978 it was greeted almost with relief that at last the waiting and uncertainty were over. For some it was the end of a way of life which they could not face: Joe Dacruz, who worked aa a pipe fitter in the steel works until it closed, remembers a workmate who committed suicide. "When they shut the works, he had no job, and without that work he was lost."

The end was surprisingly quick. The last iron was cast on 7th April, and the last billet rolled some three weeks later. Tom Keen, who had started his working life on the shop floor of East Moors, remembers attending the ceremonial last cast of iron in his capacity as Managing Director of GKN South Wales. He found it an emotional experience, watching workmen whose families had worked together for generations, exchanging addresses on pieces of cardboard in order to keep in touch. When it came to seeing off the last billet he decided to decline the invitation, but when the time came he put on his mack, left his office in GKN and walked across the railway track to join in unofficially.

During demolition:
the flattened site.

Within months the demolition workers had taken over and done what Lord Melchet had said they would do on that December day six years before – they flattened the site. Most of them were men from the works; J J Sullivan, who had been a furnaceman, was one of them. "They had me to blow the furnace up. I pressed the button and blew it to pieces."

The demolition of the blast furnaces at East Moors.

CASTLE WORKS AND TREMORFA

But though the skyline of Cardiff looked strangely depleted without the grey furnaces and chimneys of East Moors, and at night the docks area seemed oddly quiet and dark, steelmaking in the city was by no means dead. Out at Tremorfa the new steelworks, whose size belies the name of mini-mill, had for some time been in production, as had the new rod mill at Castle works. Both were officially opened by the Prince of Wales in 1977, amid much trumpeting of the fact that they were among the most modern plant in Europe.

But the late seventies were difficult years for GKN as well. Profits fell steadily after 1974, partly because of problems in the motor industry, in which the company had become increasingly involved. Within the space of a few short years it became clear that the steel industry as a whole was suffering from over-capacity: partly the result, according to Malcolm Wallace, of small and newly-independent countries seeing the establishment of a steel works (along with an airline) as being a symbol of national virility. Governments which had once purchased steel products were now subsidising their own steel industries, so that cheap steel was flooding an increasingly overcrowded market.

Steps were taken to re-structure the management of the company, so that GKN South Wales became part of the division known as GKN Rolled and Bright.

The new rod mill with East Bute Dock in the foreground, August 1979.

This division was experiencing considerable difficulties, not least because of initial problems at both the rod mill and the steel works. Despite the trumpeting, production at the rod mill was disappointing. According to John Collier, who initially turned down the offer of the job of managing it but then offered to help sort out the problems, this was partly because of design faults for which no-one would take responsibility, and partly because of the comparative inexperience of the young workforce. In the days of full employment young people could afford to be less settled, and were more likely to move on, so there was a high turnover which, coupled with general overmanning, led to poor standards overall. "Altogether it turned out to be a bit of a shambles," John Collier recalls somewhat ruefully.

The situation was not much better at Tremorfa, where the first cast from the new electric arc mini-mill was tapped in September 1976. Here the general manager was Paul Rich, who had already had experience of setting up a brand new works in Ireland, as part of a GKN consultancy. The Tremorfa site was not ideal, especially since the steelworks had to be laid down by the side of existing mills. Nevertheless the savings in cost were huge when compared with East Moors, mostly because the workforce was so much smaller. Many of the people recruited had worked in East Moors – not altogether a good thing, Paul Rich believes now. "To some extent I think we imported some entrenchment in thinking that we would have been better without." However the initial problems were more to do with engineering. "Some of the plant and equipment we had didn't perform, and with four or five problems at once it was pretty difficult."

As the decade ended and the world demand for steel and steel products decreased still further it was clear that radical steps were needed if the British re-rolling industry was to survive at all. The workforce had at all levels become complacent. Managers were convinced that prices could be forced no lower. They could only think in terms of the return of growing markets, where customers were queueing up for their products. So many layers of management existed that concepts of individual accountability and responsibility were completely alien: there was always another department somewhere which could sort a problem out. On the shop floor there was the comforting thought that whatever happened to the company's fortunes was the responsibility of management.

DRASTIC MEASURES

The arrival of Alan Cox as Chairman of the division was salutary. Originally an accountant by profession, he had considerable experience of troubleshooting within GKN. "He came in with a businessman's view of it," Roger Evans, then a senior manager, recalls: "At the time when he arrived the whole world changed for us in Cardiff." Alan Cox makes no bones about his first reactions. "I was appalled," he says; at the number of people for ever walking around Castle works "like a Lowry painting"; at the ten million pounds worth of stock in the central stores "and not one of sixty engineers claiming responsibility"; at the bad housekeeping which meant "walking through three yards of water with tin cans in it" to a senior manager's office; at the lack of analysis of performance – "no-one knew what they should be able to achieve in terms of tonnes per hour or electricity consumption or tonnes of finished product out of so many tonnes of material." Most of all he was appalled at the lack of awareness of the huge losses that were being made. "I think the average man working in the company had no idea what trouble he was in."

They soon found out. Within a short time the whole ethos of the company changed as people discovered that unless they accepted new styles of management and production there would simply be no jobs left. Long lunch breaks and whole layers of status-conscious managers had to go, as had restrictive practices on the shop floor. Incredibly, the special bus service to

Rogerstone was still operating – more than forty years after the closure of the works there. It cost some £4000 a year and was for five people. No-one had questioned its continuation.

Morale was low – "base minus ten", according to Roger Evans, who as a senior manager was excluded from the directors' conferences and sensed his colleagues' unease. "There was real fear about. We knew there were big conferences and meetings to discuss how to make a success out of a business that was losing money. Everybody was very suspicious; various thinking people were concerned there wasn't a future at all."

Sadly for many this was true. If the business was to survive, if efficiency was to be achieved, the workforce had to be reduced. Alan Cox reasoned that if people were to be well-informed about what they were doing and were to take responsibility for it, then the old highly centralised structure was not necessary. Managers needed to be physically close to the mills where manufacturing took place, and they should be concerned with the people who worked there, rather than with some remote and non-specialist central organisation. As a consequence the whole of the central organisation of GKN South Wales was dismantled, and its functions distributed to its component parts: the rod mill, the nail factory, the bar mill and so on.

Cover of one of the leaflets that accompanied GKN's Report and Accounts in 1980. Inside the figures plainly show losses and employees are urged to co-operate in making the new company successful.

THE CUTTING OF LOSSES

Meanwhile talks of varying degrees of secrecy were once again taking place. The directors of GKN lacked the instinctive commitment of their predecessors to heavy steel, yet they had recently invested heavily in the Tremorfa steel works and the Cardiff rod mill, both of which were now losing money. BSC was losing even more, and in opening the Scunthorpe rod mill without closing anything down had exacerbated the situation by increasing capacity and surplus output. GKN could not compete with a nationalised undertaking which was prepared

Cobbled steel: steel billets looping between two stands of rolls. An unusual photograph taken at the new Rod Mill on the first day of operation.

and able to sustain such losses, and under a Labour government would have been prepared and probably able to sell off its loss-making steel producing plant to BSC.

The new Conservative government under Margaret Thatcher, however, was keen to dissociate itself from the nationalised industries, and Alan Cox remembers GKN being offered the whole of BSC by Sir Keith Joseph. The offer was refused, but it was in this climate that the scheme known as Phoenix One was launched. Instead of competing with each other, the re-rolling and heavy steel activities of GKN and BSC were to be combined in an independent venture. In practice that meant that the whole of GKN's South Wales activities, (Castle Works and the various plant at the Tremorfa site) together with various other steel processing plant in other parts of the country, were to be joined with BSC's Scunthorpe rod mill to form a new company which was to be called Allied Steel and Wire Ltd.

PART FIVE: THE PHOENIX –
ALLIED STEEL AND WIRE

I t was the formation of a new company, which could establish a new culture and new ways of working which was to save steelmaking for Cardiff. Freed from the dead hand of a remote and centralised organisation, and having through necessity to break with past practices in order to survive at all, the new management teams were able to concentrate on turning round the flagging fortunes which had for too long been associated with steelmaking. In this final part we shall see how this was done, and how Allied Steel and Wire has established itself not only as a leading manufacturer of steel and steel products, but also as an integral part of the development of Cardiff as one of Britain's most attractive cities.

THE NEW TEAM

Allied Steel and Wire was formed on 29th June 1981, with Alan Cox as its Chief Executive. Some members of the main GKN board, perhaps loath to lose the services of a young and energetic director, would have preferred him to be seconded to the new company. He, however, was adamant that he should make a public commitment to the new concern, and resigned from GKN. Malcolm Wallace, the new company's managing director, had been commercial director of GKN (South Wales). Unlike Alan Cox, whose contact with steelmaking was limited to his few years in Cardiff, Malcolm Wallace had spent all his working life on the Cardiff steel sites. They were thus a promising team: the financial experience of the one balanced by the commercial and industrial experience of the other. "Between the pair of us we pretty well covered everything," Malcolm

Wallace remembers. "Basically we were very fortunate. We had no head office on our backs because we were head office, and we had a very modern steel works and two very modern rod mills. All the major units, the things that made up the kit, were good." What was more, they had the support of experienced senior managers who realised that the cosy world of GKN had gone for ever.

Nevertheless the outlook must have been daunting. At the beginning the new group was losing money fast – £3 million in the first six months. And there could be no turning back. Since GKN had contributed the majority of the plant for the new venture, BSC put up £40 million to make up its half share. It was made clear, moreover, that this was the final contribution: the new government was opposed to any kind of state support for industry, and if the enterprise foundered there could be no extra cash. No wonder Malcolm Wallace admits to being "nervous and excited," – apparently one of the merchant bankers remarked that the deal could not be faulted but he nevertheless predicted bankruptcy in eighteen months.

There were some hopeful signs, however. Alan Cox's policy of finding out as much as possible about the company had shown him that costs could be cut enormously. Secondly, BSC's closure of several small rod mills in the late seventies had eliminated some of the over-capacity, and since ASW now owned the Scunthorpe rod mill there was much less competition from within Britain. Finally, both Malcolm Wallace and Alan Cox were aware that in the Tremorfa Steelworks and the Cardiff rod mill they had up-to-date technology which was capable of efficient production. "It was a good kit."

They had, too, an enormous psychological advantage. They were able to say to the workforce that they had to succeed or go under. There would be no more money from the government, and none from GKN or BSC either.

A solution had to be found to the fact that other companies had the same plant as ASW and yet were operating it profitably, and if ASW were to survive it was clear that there was going to have to be change at all levels. They were going to have to adopt what was to become a familiar slogan within the company – world's best practice. "I needed to know what was the best in the world," said Alan Cox. "I've always been a fanatic of competition; I wanted to know what the competition was doing, how good they were and how good we could be."

Like most winning ideas it has the virtue of simplicity. An important first step had in fact already been taken: a group of engineers, led by Roy Stewartson, had been dispatched all over the world to look at other steel companies which had similar plant, to see what their production and cost levels were, and to ascertain how those levels could be achieved.

Their findings were remarkable. As part of the exercise senior managers had been asked to estimate by how much they could increase profitability if a wand were to be waved so that there were no problems connected with production at all. To their amazement they found that the figures achieved by steelmakers abroad, some of them competitors, were greatly higher than the ones they were even dreaming about. "That was a big shock," said Alan Cox. "It was quite clear that we weren't even thinking in the same terms as our competitors. We had to change the whole culture."

Changing people's attitudes and beliefs is notoriously difficult, but the senior management team reasoned that if they themselves had been converted to a different way of thinking by colleagues who had actually seen the ways in which such productivity was achieved, then the best way to convert everyone else was to send them to see with their own eyes too.

THE JAPANESE EXPERIENCE

Not surprisingly, it had emerged that the steel companies which were most efficient were in Japan. Malcolm Wallace and Alan Cox attended an international steelmaking conference in Toronto, where they were able to meet delegations from various Japanese companies. They hoped to be able to reach agreement about reciprocal sharing of technical expertise, while at the same time arranging for people from Cardiff to visit plant in Japan. At first the Japanese

Alan Cox (centre) and Roy Stewartson taking park in a Japanese tea ceremony at Brook House, inherited from GKN and now used by ASW for entertaining guests.

were perhaps understandably suspicious, and had to be convinced that ASW would not be competing with them, but eventually Kobe Steel, which operates a rod mill almost identical to those at Castle Works and Scunthorpe, gave a favourable response. Within a day Sumitomo Steel had made a similar offer, only to be told they were too late. However it turned out that a subsidiary of Sumitomo, Kyoei, operated a mini-mill very similar to that in Tremorfa. Within months the first groups were on their way, under the aegis of Roy Stewartson, who eased the way considerably by forming firm friendships with several of the Japanese.

Inevitably the exercise was successful. Seeing with one's own eyes is a powerful persuader, and far more effective than company seminars or lectures by management. "When they'd actually seen a steel works and a rod mill working in the way they'd been told," said Malcolm Wallace, "When they could actually touch it and see it and ask about it, then they were convinced." The Japanese had supposed that their visitors would all be managers, but in practice many shopfloor workers joined the parties that went out, first from the rod mill and then from the steelworks. Les Crocker, now a pulpit operator in the rod mill, was one of them: "It was amazing to see the place working there. There was nothing different, yet the mill just kept going; all the time I was there I only saw one cobble. They were checking, monitoring all the time. We were always rushing about, sorting out cobbles, getting the mill running again, but they never had that because there were no cobbles, which is more like we are now. We are starting to check and monitor things so we don't get as many cobbles." The same thing applied to management , according to Paul Rich: "The problem is that here managers manage problem situations, instead of applying their intellect to find out why the situation happened in the first place."

The rod mill also benefited from the assistance of a team of Japanese engineers, who visited the mills in both Cardiff and Scunthorpe. John Collier remembers: "They were commissioned to send their report back by June 1982, which they did. It was very thick and detailed and there were fifty seven recommendations. We looked at it, and some of them were justified, and some we thought we weren't ready for, like everyone wearing the same overalls. Then we took people to the training centre for a week and we told them why we'd had the Japanese over and we made the reports available for everyone to see; we didn't want any secrets. It was as much a criticism of management as anything." It was this close proximity with the Japanese, the visits and the building of relationships with them that enabled the scheme to work. Les Crocker saw the reactions change so that people were much more receptive to new ideas and prepared for change. "You've already seen things working so you know they're going to work."

Shin Miyawaki, on engineer from Kobe Steel, working with the Energy Quality Circle at Cardiff Rod Mill.

BITING THE BULLET

So much for identifying world best practice. Although it was comparatively simple to send people to Japan to observe production methods, it was still necessary to change the ideas, methods and aspirations of the workforce at all levels. Fortunately for the company the economic recession made workers at every level more willing to accept change, either in working practices or, ultimately, by accepting early retirement or even redundancy. As Malcolm Wallace said, "Everyone could see that everything was in a serious position." There was, moreover, in Margaret Thatcher "a Prime Minister who was creating an environment which encouraged management to stand up and manage more effectively than it had done before."

Uncomfortable decisions had to be made. Decentralisation meant that people who were used to the comparative anonymity of a large firm were forced to accept responsibility in businesses which were small enough for there to be nowhere to hide from it. Costs and manning levels had to be constantly justified. The unions, realising that if this operation went to the wall there would be nothing to replace it, and at the same time unable to deny the experience of their own members who had seen lower manning levels in Japan, agreed to stand apart from national agreements and to negotiate directly with the company. Such was their co-operation that not one hour, according to Alan Cox, was lost through disputes.

Yet the workforce, management included, had to be reduced. Redundant buildings were demolished, including the now empty GKN general offices at Castle Works, which were replaced by gardens. Apart from practical considerations, this had two psychological effects. In the first place, the physical remains of the old central organisation were removed, and secondly, the shrubs and flowers provided a much pleasanter atmosphere for people to work in. The

Young graduates outside the new conference centre.

old canteen building, which had once housed several separate canteens carefully graded according to status, was re-designed and eventually became a modern conference centre. The businesses "were sent back to the blue sheds" – that is, to the places where manufacturing was carried out. These were separate profit centres, so that the efficiency of each could be more readily ascertained. Moreover, from now on there was no separation of managers from the plant they were actually managing.

FLOTATION AND INDEPENDENCE

Gradually the tide of company fortunes turned, helped not a little by a general recovery in the economy. Three years after the new company was launched GKN showed considerable interest in buying it back: far from moving in that direction the directors wanted yet more independence. An independent chairman was appointed and Warburgs, the merchant bankers, were called in to offer advice. They suggested a two-stage bid for independence. First of all, the institutions would have to be persuaded to buy major shareholdings off GKN and BSC, and then eventually the company could be floated on the Stock Exchange.

Furthermore, in order to show their commitment when the institutions moved in, senior management was asked to take a stake in the company, a daunting prospect to most, who had to borrow to finance their investment. "It was the price of freedom," said Alan Cox. "If it worked, you might make some money. But I'd been brought up in Birmingham and I'd never been in debt in my life. I hated it." "I wasn't rich, and if the company had failed I'd have lost my house," Roger Evans said, and he was not alone. But by this time people had seen the company succeed, and were prepared to take risks. GKN was bought out, and BSC retained only 20% of the total shareholding.

This was still not a public company, however, which it would need to be in order to raise more capital. Alan Cox and Malcolm Wallace had been given to believe that there would have to be a time lag between the buy-out from BSC and GKN before flotation could take place, especially since, as the flotation of a steel company was a very rare event, there was not much City experience to draw on. Alan Cox remembered spending the best part of two years in the City, leaving the running of the company to the increasingly confident senior management. His efforts paid off: it was in fact only a matter of months before the bankers suggested flotation, which eventually took place on 2nd June, 1988. Its success was an indication that the financial world recognised the viability of steelmaking in Cardiff for the foreseeable future.

The confidence of the business world has been gained by achieving efficiency, and although that is closely linked with work practices it also depends on a willingness to keep abreast of technological change.

TECHNOLOGICAL DEVELOPMENTS

Although the essential technology of the furnaces at Tremorfa has remained the same, its efficiency has been greatly increased by technical changes. The lining of the furnace with water cooled panels has meant not only that more electric power can be used to speed the steelmaking process, but also that the

An employee pleased with his investment.

furnace has to be re-lined less often. Also, the time from one tap to the next has been greatly reduced. The introduction of foaming slag into the furnace absorbs the damaging glare from the electric arc and enables it to be left on full power for longer, while a new transformer has increased the amount of power available. Furthermore, once the initial charge has been made and most of the carbon has been driven off, the molten steel is tapped into a ladle furnace, which has a much lower power input but where time can be taken to refine the steel while the big furnace melts scrap again. Colin Ceshion, who still works at Tremorfa, sums it up: "When I started at Tremorfa it would take three hours to tap the furnace. Well, now we have tapped in an hour and five minutes, and more tonnage. Now there is more steel, fewer people, less time, less power." Indeed, there is now more steel made in a year at Tremorfa than ever there was at East Moors.

Nothing so dramatic has happened at the rod mill, except that the original four strands, rolled from four billets simultaneously, have now been reduced to two, and at the moment produce more rod than was predicted for the original design. Les Crocker has noticed the difference: "There is less than half the

The pulpit operator in the rod mill overlooks the roughing train and has computers to help him.

Skills training at ASW's Training Centre.

workforce producing twice as much as when it was four strands." In fact, the yearly output of the rod mill operating on two strands is approaching the total envisaged for fully efficient four strand operation. Both the control of the mill and the operation of the furnace have been computerised, and most recently steps are being taken to ensure that the coiled rod is presented to the customer in properly formed coils that will withstand pressure in storage.

THE NEW MANAGERS

There is a determination within the company not only to keep abreast of the latest technical developments and management strategies, but also to maintain and recruit a workforce which is enthusiastic and unafraid of change. Although the days of apprenticeships are long gone, there is great emphasis on training and also on the sponsorship and recruitment of graduates, which Alan Cox regards as an act of faith: "You had to believe when ASW started that we could recruit more and more young people from universities. We need to have this quality coming through." Gill Knowles was one of the first. She spent a year in ASW before being sponsored by the company at Imperial College London, where she gained a master's degree in engineering. She then joined the company's graduate training scheme, doing projects in various parts of the works. "I did a project at Allied Bar Coaters and it must have been some use to them, because it was all about how they should extend their plant, which is exactly what they've done, so that was good." At the age of twenty eight she is now a senior manager in the nail factory. " I'm lucky because I really enjoy my work. I'm part of the management team, and I'm responsible for all the manufacturing side, all the production, the buying, the machines."

ASW AND THE COMMUNITY

From the very first the new company had to establish itself within the local community, not only in Splott and Tremorfa but also within Cardiff as a whole.

Alan Cox with graduates at Brook House.

There was still a yawning gap left by the demolition of East Moors, both physically and psychologically, and now the GKN connection was to vanish as well. There was a firm belief that the company shoud take its responsibilities as the largest manufacturer in Cardiff seriously, and sponsorship was forthcoming for a wide variety of local projects and activities as well as for the arts. Links were established with not only with local schools but with others all over South Glamorgan, and individual businesses were encouraged to become involved in local events. Money was forthcoming to help youngsters at Glamorgan County Cricket Club, and increasingly employees are able to find sponsorship for courses which they follow in their own time.

John Metcalf, a local composer sponsored by ASW, working with pupils from the Bishop of Llandaff School, Cardiff.

In this sort of activity the company has more in common with the Guests of Dowlais than with its GKN predecessors, for although ASW has interests and and businesses outside Cardiff it is here that the heart of the company lies. Situated as the rod mill is in the heart of the old docklands, ASW is inextricably bound up with the future of the area, as is manifest by Alan Cox's membership of the board of Cardiff Bay Development Corporation.

ASW TODAY

At any time it would be difficult to give an enduring description of a company as committed to change as Allied Steel and Wire. With each set of annual reports the different groupings and structures of the businesses show fresh evidence of adaptability, and there is an increasingly confident air as the basic philosophies prove themselves. Recent developments have included the establishment of a new division to produce specialised building systems (ASW Construction Systems), and the acquisition of Allied Bird Fragmentation, which processes steel scrap for the electric arc furnace. Meanwhile the making of steel and the rolling of rods, bars and sections, which are fundamental to the group's success and whose development has formed a continuous thread throughout this

Night working at Allied Bird Fragmentation, where steel scrap for the electric arc furnace is processed.

narrative, are carried out with ever greater efficiency. Names which have become familiar as the story has unfolded still survive: Castle Wire next to the Cardiff Rod Mill, Castle Nails and Somerset Wire at the Tremorfa site.

But it is not only the names which have survived. The activities which are carried out in the various works and mills are recognisably developments of the technologies first developed on Dowlais Top, and were Sir John and Lady Charlotte Guest to be transported there today they would soon recognise them as such. Lady Charlotte's thrill at the noise and flaring heat of the furnace, and Sir John's fascination with the practicalities of production find echoes in many people today, and so too does their recognition that the maintenance of a profitable manufacturing company benefits not only the industrialists but the communities of which they are a part, and to which they are responsible.

The aim of this story has been to show how these links have been maintained, not only by tracking the technological and commercial developments but also by letting a few of the people involved speak for themselves. The Dowlais works in Merthyr and Cardiff have long since disappeared, and the old Castle Works lies beneath the Alcan factory in Rogerstone, but there are people alive who remember them, and whose memories form part of that thread which links the furnace that the first John Guest managed on Dowlais Top with the electric arcs of Tremorfa.